For condi

Respiratory Metabolism in Plants

HARPER REPRINT SERIES
IN PLANT PHYSIOLOGY

RESPIRATORY METABOLISM

IN PLANTS

Harry Beevers

Professor of Plant Physiology
Department of Biological Sciences
Purdue University

jointly published by
HARPER & ROW, New York, Evanston & London
and JOHN WEATHERHILL, INC., Tokyo

257956

Preface

In this, the second monograph of the series, the present status of our knowledge of respiratory metabolism in plants is reviewed, with the needs of honors and graduate students in mind. No attempt has been made to cover all aspects of respiration in plants. Instead, a factual presentation of the biochemical events which have been shown to occur in higher plants and which are conceivably of importance in respiration is given. An assessment is then made of the experimental evidence for their participation and importance *in vivo* and for the interplay with other metabolic events going on in plant cells.

Harry Beevers

Lafayette, Indiana
September, 1960

Abbreviations

ADP	adenosine diphosphate
ATP	adenosine triphosphate
CoA	coenzyme A
DNP	2,4-dinitrophenol
DPN	diphosphopyridine nucleotide
DPNH	diphosphopyridine nucleotide (reduced)
EMP	Embden-Meyerhof-Parnas glycolytic sequence
GSSG	glutathione (oxidized)
GSH	glutathione (reduced)
iP	inorganic phosphate
-(P)	$-H_2PO_3$
$\sim$P	"energy-rich" phosphate center
PN	phosphopyridine nucleotide
PNH	phosphopyridine nucleotide (reduced)
P/O	micromoles phosphate esterified/microatoms oxygen absorbed
$Q_{O_2}(N)$	mm^3 O_2 uptake/hr/mg protein N
R.Q.	respiratory quotient
TCA cycle	tricarboxylic acid cycle
TPN	triphosphopyridine nucleotide
TPNH	triphosphopyridine nucleotide (reduced)
TPP	thiamine pyrophosphate

NOTE: Whenever a compound having ionizable groups is mentioned in the text, it should be realized that it will be more or less dissociated according to the prevailing pH conditions. No attempt has been made in the abbreviations and structural formulae to show what the major ionic form is at so-called "physiological" pH levels; only the undissociated forms are used.

Contents

LIST OF FIGURES

LIST OF TABLES

Chapter 1

Introduction

In plants, as in other organisms, respiration involves the oxidative breakdown of certain organic substrates normally present in the cells. When these cells have access to air, as they usually do, O_2 uptake and CO_2 output are the external manifestations of this process, and so long as the study of plant respiration was limited to following gas exchanges without regard to the internal events, the process could be simply defined. A great deal of data has been collected about the gas exchanges of various plant parts under a wide range of external conditions. At the same time, analytical work and feeding experiments have established that sucrose or its component hexoses—the major free sugars in plants—are the usual substrates for respiration in most plant cells. This core of information representing the beginning and end of the respiration process poses the problem with which this review is primarily concerned, namely, the mechanisms by which sugars are respired to CO_2 and H_2O in plants and the interrelationships which have become apparent between this process and various others going on at the same time in plant cells.

Over the past thirty years, and particularly during the past decade, an increasing amount of information has been forthcoming on these dynamic biochemical events underlying respiration in plants. To be sure, the gathering of this information has in large part lagged a few years behind, and has frequently followed the directions established by, similar activity of workers engaged with cells of animals and some microorganisms. Nevertheless, the outcome is not unimpressive. Although formidable problems remain, experimental evidence is now at hand to construct a coherent picture of intermediary respiratory metabolism in plant cells without depending seriously on unproven analogies. An important result of this kind

1

of research has been the definition of many points of contact and interchange with other kinds of metabolic events going on in cells—so much so that it may seriously be questioned whether it is justifiable to dissect out a part of the total machinery, to assign to it a respiratory role, and to consider it in isolation from the rest.

Certainly the ramifications of hexose dissimilation which have become apparent make it impossible to regard the paths of breakdown as leading inevitably to CO_2. These breakdown sequences lead not only to the production of energy in a utilizable form but at the same time to precursors of cellular materials which in younger cells may account for the diversion of a large fraction of the carbon of the starting substrate (Chapter 10). These inextricable connections with other metabolic processes and the different usages which have been adopted in the past (for a summary see James, 1953, Chapter I) make it difficult and perhaps pointless to attempt a hard and fast definition of respiration which would be acceptable to all plant physiologists. O_2 uptake which occurs as the normal accompaniment of breakdown of hexoses and other materials in higher plants is the aspect of the process which is most frequently used as an operational definition. It has long been realized of course that the important functional aspect of the process is the provision of energy in a utilizable form during the breakdown of more complex to simpler molecules. To this we must now add that the intermediates which are produced may also be used for synthetic events going on at the same time. If we use the term so widely as to include "all those material changes undergone by complex cellular substances . . . which lead to a diminution in free energy" (James, 1953), we stand in danger of including all metabolic changes in the scope of the definition.

It is now customary to use "fermentation" in place of the older term "anaerobic respiration," which may be considered self-contradictory. By fermentation we mean the breakdown of substrates which leads, *inter alia,* to the accumulation of products such as alcohol which are not immediately utilizable by the tissue. We may note that this kind of breakdown can be induced by conditions other than anaerobiosis (Chapter 2) and leads to the production of small amounts of utilizable energy.

Experimental data about rates of respiration in different plant parts, responses to moisture, temperature, inorganic nutrients, excision, starvation, and other treatments are to be found in a very large and scattered literature. No attempt is made here to review this vast amount of information; the reader is referred to a recent handbook (Dittmer and Grebe, 1958) in which a valuable compilation and a bibliography are presented by a group of plant physiologists. Appraisals of pertinent papers on some of these aspects of the process are also presented by Stiles and Leach (1952), in standard texts, and more recently in W. O. James's important book on plant respiration (1953), which should be consulted for an exhaustive treatment of physiological matters. It should be recognized that a complete understanding of respiratory metabolism at the cellular level would provide a sufficient basis for accounting for the large variations in respiratory rate which have been observed and for the responses to external variables.

We may note that in the past decade there have been some innovations in the actual measurement of respiratory rates. The use of infrared gas analysis for CO_2 and automatically recording O_2-measuring devices have greatly simplified the collection of respiratory data from large samples of tissue. Measurements of changes in conductivity or pH of an alkaline solution through which an air stream is passed from the respiratory chamber have allowed precise and continuous recording of respiration drifts. Polarographic methods for O_2 have been used in determinations on very small amounts of material, for which Cartesian divers and other sensitive devices have also been exploited.

Even so, standard manometric measurements have provided the great bulk of the data on plant respiration in the past ten years. When this method is used with tissue amenable to accurate sampling, the results are considerably more clear cut and satisfying than many in the older literature. For example, some results on the effects of O_2 tension and temperature on the respiration of onion root tips are shown in Figure 1. As the temperature is lowered, O_2 saturation is achieved at lower partial pressures; we note that under these conditions maximum rates of O_2 uptake are not attained at 30° C with air as the gas phase. At any given O_2 level the familiar effect of changing temperature on respiration rate is shown, and when adequate O_2 is present, the Q_{10} in the range 20°–30° is greater than 2. At each temperature, as the O_2 uptake becomes curtailed by lowering the O_2 tension, the R.Q. values rise above unity. The O_2 uptake values observed at 35° indicate that this temperature is above the optimal one for aerobic respiration. We may note, however, that CO_2 output is not adversely affected, and this might indicate a partially selective effect of the relatively high temperature. Other indications that glycolysis is less susceptible than subsequent events comes from the work of Oota *et al.* (1956) on *Vigna sesquipedalis*. Here again, at higher temperatures, high R.Q. values (and alcohol production) were a feature of the metabolism. Moreover, in this seedling additional effects of temperature were noted, since at the lower temperatures a higher proportion of fat than of starch was used as respiratory substrate. As the temperature was increased above 25° this situation was reversed.

It will be recalled that striking responses to temperature of the levels of soluble sugars, particularly sucrose, were a feature of Barker's (1933) classical investigations on the respiration of the potato tuber. It became clear from this work that the pace of reactions converting starch, the storage form of carbohydrate, into readily utilizable sugars may under some conditions limit the respiratory rate. The early depletion of free sugars and polysaccharides in many starvation experiments and the fact that declining respiratory rates can frequently be restored by the addition of glucose, fructose, or sucrose (see James, 1953) point unmistakably to the participation of these compounds as major respiratory fuels.

Recent work on enzymes which can interconvert various sugars by way of their phosphorylated derivatives and experiments with various labeled sugars have emphasized the ready

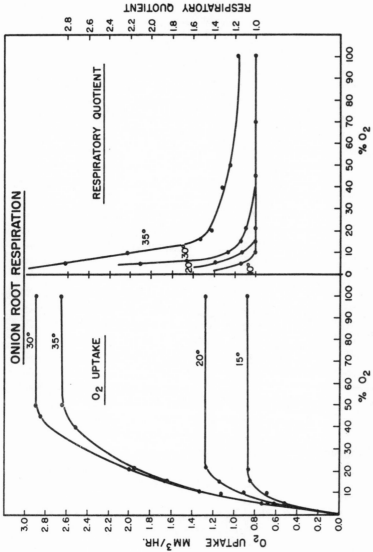

FIGURE 1.—Effects of temperature and O_2 tension on the respiration of onion root tips. (Drawn from data of Berry and Norris, 1949.)

interconversion which may occur, although it is also clear that separate pools may exist (e.g., Porter and May, 1955), so that all of the soluble sugars may not be immediately and equally available as substrates for respiration.

The earlier investigations showed that respiration may be supported by a variety of compounds (e.g., Spoehr and Mc-Gee, 1923), but these observations do not of course imply that several entirely different pathways exist. To the extent that a given compound is itself, or can be readily converted by the tissue into, an intermediate of the sequences outlined in subsequent chapters, it will be respired along with the intermediate arising from the true substrate—always provided, of course, that it gains access to the respiratory centers. Recent work with C^{14}-labeled materials has made it clear that a variety of compounds related to respiratory intermediates are actually metabolized and do not act merely as stimulants of the respiratory sequence without themselves being used up in the process (see Thomas et al., 1957). Thus, for example, glycerol, pyruvate, and acids of the TCA cycle have been shown to be utilized (Chapter 3), and the ability of plant tissues to deal oxidatively with gluconate and some pentoses (Chapter 2) has been established. The oxidative breakdown of compounds such as acetate, glutamate, and alanine is brought about because these compounds are readily converted into known respiratory intermediates. These experiments show that even when food reserves such as proteins and fats are being utilized the pathways of dissimilation may be ones which are also utilized—in part—during the respiration of sugars.

Considerable importance has been attached to the respiratory quotient (R.Q.) in earlier work on respiratory substrates, and there is no doubt that the nature of the substrate usually determines what the value of the quotients is. The frequency with which values close to unity have been observed (James, 1953, Chapter IV) attests to the part played by sugars as the respiratory substrate in plant tissues. In recent years, however, reactions linking respiration with other events in the cell have been established, and it has become clear that these may have repercussions on the R.Q. Appreciable changes from unity might result even though sugars continue to furnish the substrate. Some of these considerations are:

1. Incomplete oxidation of the sugar due to a diversion in synthetic events of respiratory intermediates with oxidation levels different from the original substrate (Chapter 10).
2. Reductive events such as sulphate and nitrate reduction, reductive syntheses (Chapter 9).
3. Oxidations and decarboxylations unrelated to respiration proper.
4. The retention of respired CO_2 in tissue fluids.
5. Nonphotosynthetic carboxylation reactions leading to acid accumulation. The acid fluctuations in succulents have, because of their magnitude, attracted most attention, but the elucidation of these reactions (see, e.g., Ranson and Thomas, 1960) and the general distribution of carboxylating enzymes in plants make the pickup of CO_2 a general possibility to be reckoned with. Experiments with $C^{14}O_2$ show in fact that such carboxylation reactions are of wide occurrence, and they achieve sizable proportions in some tissues other than succulents (e.g., germinating fatty seedlings and roots in certain salt solutions; see Chapter 8).

In addition to the above, the persistence of detectable fermentation in some tissues, e.g., senescent fruits, even when these are in air, has been recognized as a cause of high R.Q. values. It is frequently assumed that in bulky tissues, such as potato tubers, O_2 levels are sufficiently subnormal to induce some fermentation, but actual measurements (Burton, 1950) indicate that O_2 levels are not in fact limiting (see Laties, 1957, for a valuable discussion). Temporary high R.Q.'s due to alcoholic fermentation are a feature of the germination of some seeds in which the access of O_2 is limited by the tissues surrounding the embryo. In addition, even in actively growing tissues there may be alcohol accumulation. Betz (1955, 1957, 1958) has shown this to be so in corn root tips. An al-

Part I

The Respiratory Mechanism

Chapter 2

Initial Stages

of Glucose Catabolism

The reactions by which 1 mole of glucose is converted into 2 of pyruvate are commonly referred to as the Embden-Meyerhof-Parnas (EMP) sequence after three of the many leading biochemists who contributed to its elucidation. The individual steps in this glycolytic pathway, which is found in all biological groups, were first worked out in experiments with yeast and muscle preparations. The interesting history of the development of this knowledge will not be dealt with here; the reader is referred to Harden's (1923) volume and to articles in Sumner and Myrback's compendium (1951). Many of the individual enzymes from yeast and muscle have been purified to the stage of crystallization, and methods for their assay have been precisely worked out (see Colowick and Kaplan, 1955). An outline of the reactions of the EMP sequence (Figure 2) as they are presently understood will be given, and evidence for its all-important role in plant respiration will be discussed. James's group in Oxford carried out some of the first definitive work with glycolytic systems in plants (see James, 1953). In the late 1940's Stumpf and his colleagues carried out a sustained attack on the enzymes from peas, using sensitive methods which had by then become available (Stumpf, 1952). All of the enzymes concerned have now been individually demonstrated in plants (Axelrod and Bandurski, 1953); some have been intensively purified and their properties examined in detail.

Glucose is here regarded as the starting point of glycolysis, although it is clear that entry into the sequence can be made at other levels, depending on what the respiratory substrate is. Thus, for example, phosphorylated hexoses may be formed from phosphorylase action on starch or from fructose produced hydrolytically from sucrose or larger fructans, and triose phosphate may originate from glycerol.

Phosphorylation of glucose* and its conversion to fructose-1,6-diphosphate. The first reaction, catalyzed by hexokinase, is a phosphorylation at the expense of ATP, with glucose-6-phosphate as the product:

$$
\begin{array}{c}
\text{CHO} \\
| \\
\text{HCOH} \\
| \\
\text{HOCH} \\
| \\
\text{HCOH} \\
| \\
\text{HCOH} \\
| \\
\text{CH}_2\text{OH} \\
\text{Glucose}
\end{array}
\quad + \text{ATP} \xrightarrow[\text{Hexokinase}]{\text{Mg}^{++}}
\begin{array}{c}
\text{CHO} \\
| \\
\text{HCOH} \\
| \\
\text{HOCH} \\
| \\
\text{HCOH} \\
| \\
\text{HCOH} \\
| \\
\text{CH}_2\text{O(P)} \\
\text{Glucose-6-phosphate}
\end{array}
\quad + \text{ADP} + \text{H}^+ \quad (1)
$$

The reaction is strongly exergonic, and an excess of hexokinase is frequently used experimentally as an efficient trap for the terminal phosphate group of ATP. However, it can also be shown that glucose-6-phosphate itself inhibits the hexokinase, so that a self-regulating system may be set up under natural conditions. Hexokinase activity is frequently found to be associated with plant mitochondria (Millerd *et al.*, 1951; Biale *et al.*, 1957), and the properties of the wheat-germ enzyme have been examined by Saltman (1953).

The glucose-6-phosphate is subject to phosphohexoisomerase, which maintains an equilibrium between this substance and fructose-6-phosphate (Reaction 2):

---

* Unless otherwise indicated, it will be assumed that the sugars have the D-configuration.

$$
\begin{array}{ccc}
\text{CHO} & & \text{CH}_2\text{OH} \\
| & & | \\
\text{HCOH} & & \text{C}{=}\text{O} \\
| & & | \\
\text{HOCH} & & \text{HOCH} \\
| & \xrightarrow{\ \ \text{Phosphohexoisomerase}\ \ } & | \\
\text{HCOH} & & \text{HCOH} \\
| & & | \\
\text{HCOH} & & \text{HCOH} \\
| & & | \\
\text{CH}_2\text{O(P)} & & \text{CH}_2\text{O(P)}
\end{array}
\qquad (2)
$$

Glucose-6-phosphate (70%)   Fructose-6-phosphate (30%)

The conversion of fructose-6-phosphate to fructose-1,6-diphosphate requires a specific kinase and a further mole of ATP (Reaction 3). Again the equilibrium favors the accumulation of the diphosphate. Axelrod *et al.* (1952) showed that this enzyme was present in a variety of plants and described its properties. When crude plant extracts are provided with glucose, hexose diphosphate may accumulate at the expense of ATP generated in the later steps of glycolysis.

The conversion of fructose-1,6-diphosphate to two triose units (Reaction 4). This readily reversible reaction is brought about by the enzyme aldolase, which can with equal effectiveness catalyze the condensation of dihydroxyacetone phosphate with a variety of aldehydes. Tewfik and Stumpf (1949) found this enzyme in every plant tissue they examined, and Stumpf (1948) obtained a highly purified preparation from peas.

Triose phosphate isomerase brings about an equilibrium between the two trioses (Reaction 5). Its reaction is analogous to that of the phosphopentose and phosphohexose isomerases. At equilibrium, in the absence of other enzymes, the mixture contains only 3% of the aldehyde and 97% of the keto triose phosphate.

Oxidation of glyceraldehyde phosphate to (di)phosphoglyceric acid. Glyceraldehyde phosphate (or triose phosphate) dehydrogenase catalyzes the oxidation of its substrate to the corresponding acid. Three quite distinct enzymes are found in plants which can oxidize glyceraldehyde phosphate (Reac-

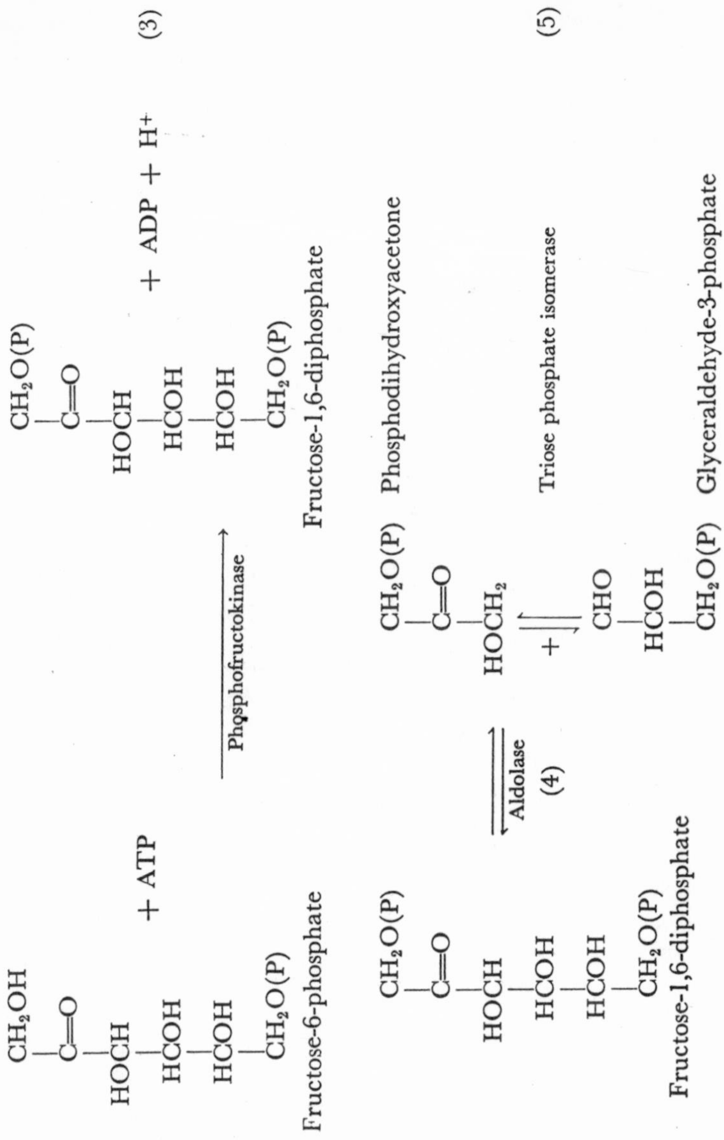

$$
\begin{array}{l}
\text{CH}_2\text{OH} \\
\,|\\
\text{C}\!=\!\text{O} \\
\,|\\
\text{HOCH} \\
\,|\\
\text{HCOH} \\
\,|\\
\text{HCOH} \\
\,|\\
\text{CH}_2\text{O(P)}
\end{array}
\;+\;\text{ATP}
\quad\xrightarrow[\text{Phosphofructokinase}]{}\quad
\begin{array}{l}
\text{CH}_2\text{O(P)} \\
\,|\\
\text{C}\!=\!\text{O} \\
\,|\\
\text{HOCH} \\
\,|\\
\text{HCOH} \\
\,|\\
\text{HCOH} \\
\,|\\
\text{CH}_2\text{O(P)}
\end{array}
\;+\;\text{ADP}\;+\;\text{H}^+
\qquad (3)
$$

Fructose-6-phosphate   Fructose-1,6-diphosphate

$$
\begin{array}{l}
\text{CH}_2\text{O(P)} \\
\,|\\
\text{C}\!=\!\text{O} \\
\,|\\
\text{HOCH} \\
\,|\\
\text{HCOH} \\
\,|\\
\text{HCOH} \\
\,|\\
\text{CH}_2\text{O(P)}
\end{array}
\quad\underset{\text{Aldolase}}{\overset{}{\rightleftharpoons}}\quad
\begin{array}{l}
\text{CH}_2\text{O(P)} \\
\,|\\
\text{C}\!=\!\text{O} \\
\,|\\
\text{HOCH}_2
\end{array}
\;+\;
\begin{array}{l}
\text{CHO} \\
\,|\\
\text{HCOH} \\
\,|\\
\text{CH}_2\text{O(P)}
\end{array}
\qquad (4)
$$

Fructose-1,6-diphosphate   Phosphodihydroxyacetone   Glyceraldehyde-3-phosphate

$$
\rightleftharpoons \qquad\qquad (5)
$$

Triose phosphate isomerase

tion 6). The first of these is a DPN-requiring dehydrogenase which is apparently quite similar to that from yeast and mammalian tissue. Tewfik and Stumpf (1951) showed that the enzyme was widespread in plant tissues, and Hageman and Arnon (1955a) have purified the enzyme extensively from peas. The details of this reaction catalyzed by the crystalline enzyme from yeast have been clarified by Racker's group (1955), and it may be presumed that the enzyme from higher plants behaves similarly. There is an initial reaction of the aldehyde with -SH groups in the enzyme, followed by a phosphorolysis of the acyl-S linkage. Arsenate can substitute for phosphate in this reaction, but the resulting 1-arseno,3-phosphoglyceric acid spontaneously decomposes to 3-phosphoglyceric acid and arsenate. This arsenolysis reaction is frequently used in assays for the enzyme. However, whereas in normal glycolysis the acyl-phosphate group of 1,3-diphosphoglycerate is of the energy-rich type and thus convertible to ATP (Reaction 7), this energy is lost as heat when arsenate is present.

An analogous enzyme, discovered more recently (Gibbs, 1952; Axelrod and Bandurski, 1952; Arnon, 1952), specifically requires TPN and is apparently confined to leaves where it coexists with the DPN enzyme. Gibbs (1955) has obtained the TPN enzyme in highly purified condition from pea shoots. Hageman and Arnon (1955b) have described the interesting fluctuations in the amounts of these two enzymes during the life cycle of the pea plant. It is possible, though not yet proved, that the TPN enzyme has to do solely with photosynthesis and is confined to the chloroplast, whereas the more widespread DPN-requiring dehydrogenase is not bound to intercellular particles and functions in respiration. Both enzymes are inhibited by iodoacetate and other SH inhibitors. A third triose phosphate dehydrogenase which co-operates with TPN but differs from the others in not requiring phosphate (or arsenate) for its activity has also been found in spinach leaves by Axelrod et al. (1953) and purified from spinach by Arnon et al. (1954). Its action results in the direct formation of 3-phosphoglycerate from 3-phosphoglyceraldehyde.

Conversion of 1,3-diphosphoglyceric acid to pyruvic acid.

$$\text{(6)}\quad
\begin{array}{l} \text{CHO} \\ \text{HCOH} + \text{iP} + \text{DPN} \\ \text{CH}_2\text{O(P)} \end{array}
\xrightarrow[\text{Glyceraldehyde phosphate dehydrogenase}]{}
\begin{array}{l} \text{COO(P)} \\ \text{HCOH} + \text{DPNH} \\ \text{CH}_2\text{O(P)} \end{array}$$

Glyceraldehyde-3-phosphate   1,3-Diphosphoglyceric acid

$$\text{(7)}\quad
\begin{array}{l} \text{COO(P)} \\ \text{HCOH} + \text{ADP} \\ \text{CH}_2\text{O(P)} \end{array}
\xrightarrow[\text{Phosphoglyceryl kinase}]{}
\begin{array}{l} \text{COOH} \\ \text{HCOH} \quad + \text{ATP} \\ \text{CH}_2\text{O(P)} \end{array}$$

1,3-Diphosphoglyceric acid   3-Phosphoglyceric acid

$$\text{(8)}\quad
\begin{array}{l} \text{COOH} \\ \text{HCOH} \\ \text{CH}_2\text{O(P)} \end{array}
\xrightarrow[\text{Phosphoglyceric mutase}]{}
\begin{array}{l} \text{COOH} \\ \text{HCO(P)} \\ \text{CH}_2\text{OH} \end{array}$$

3-Phosphoglyceric acid   2-Phosphoglyceric acid

$$\text{(9)}\quad
\begin{array}{l} \text{COOH} \\ \text{HCO(P)} \\ \text{CH}_2\text{OH} \end{array}
\xrightarrow[\text{Enolase}]{\text{Mg}^{++}}
\begin{array}{l} \text{COOH} \\ \text{CO(P)} + \text{H}_2\text{O} \\ \parallel \\ \text{CH}_2 \end{array}$$

Phospho-enol pyruvic acid

The first step in this part of the glycolytic sequence is the transfer of the phosphate residue from the acyl group of 1,3-diphosphoglycerate to ADP. Phosphoglyceryl kinase is the enzyme concerned (Reaction 7), and it has been described by Axelrod and Bandurski from peas (1953).

Phosphoglyceromutase brings about the conversion of 3-phosphoglycerate to 2-phosphoglycerate (Reaction 8), and the product is then subject to the action of enolase (Reaction 9).

The earlier work of James (1953, review) and that of Stumpf's group (1952, review) made it clear that enolase must be present in barley and pea extracts. More recently Miller (1958) has made direct investigation of the pea enzyme by spectrophotometric methods and described its properties. Like similar enzymes from other tissues, it requires Mg^{++} as a cofactor and is strikingly inhibited by fluoride. The result of the removal of water from 2-phosphoglycerate is the genera-tion of an energy-rich $(\sim P)$ center, and the phosphate is transferred to ADP in the final step in glycolysis, the products being pyruvate and ATP (Reaction 10):

$$
\begin{array}{c}
\text{COOH} \\
| \\
\text{CO(P)} + \text{ADP} \\
|| \\
\text{CH}_2 \\
\end{array}
\underset{\substack{\text{Pyruvate} \\ \text{kinase}}}{\overset{Mg^{++}K^+}{\rightleftharpoons}}
\begin{array}{c}
\text{COOH} \\
| \\
\text{C}{=}\text{O} + \text{ATP} \\
| \\
\text{CH}_3 \\
\end{array}
\qquad (10)
$$

Phospho-enol   Pyruvic
pyruvic acid   acid

This reaction, catalyzed by the pyruvate kinase, has been di-rectly demonstrated by Miller and Evans (1957) in extracts from a variety of plants, including peas. There is an absolute requirement for a divalent cation (Mg^{++} Mn^{++}) and a mono-valent cation (K^+ Rb^+ NH_4^+).

Reactions 1–10 can be summarized as follows:

Glucose $+$ 2ADP $+$ 2iP $+$ 2DPN $\rightarrow$

2 Pyruvate $+$ 2ATP $+$ 2DPNH

Under aerobic conditions the DPNH may be oxidized by a mitochondrial system with the production of up to 3 moles of ATP (Chapter 5), although oxidation by other cytoplasmic systems which are not known to generate ATP cannot be ruled out. The maximum potential yield of ATP from glycolysis with glucose as the starting point is thus 8 moles for every 2 moles of pyruvate produced.

In air, of course, pyruvate too is oxidized further, and it is in these reactions (Chapter 3) that the bulk of the energy in a form useful to the cell is produced. Normally all of the pyruvate produced in glycolysis is dealt with in this way, and there is in fact a nice gearing between pyruvate oxidation and pyruvate production (Chapter 7). However, under some conditions the rate of pyruvate production comes to exceed that of its oxidative removal. These conditions are afforded by accelerating pyruvate production (p. 62) or simply by adding an excess of pyruvate. Alternatively, pyruvate consumption can be reduced by withholding O_2 or by adding inhibitors which selectively block steps in its oxidation (pp. 60–61).

In these circumstances the pyruvate may suffer one of two alternative fates. The first and most important of these is decarboxylation to acetaldehyde by pyruvic decarboxylase (Reaction 11). This enzyme is widespread in plants, although it seems unlikely that it serves anything more than a safety-valve function under natural (i.e., aerobic) conditions. If a supply of DPNH is present, the resulting acetaldehyde is reduced by alcohol dehydrogenase to yield ethanol (Reaction 12). Alcohol dehydrogenase activity has been detected in many plant extracts both by Thunberg technique and by following DPNH oxidation on adding acetaldehyde.

$$
\begin{array}{ccc}
\text{COOH} & \text{CO}_2 & \\
| & + & \\
\text{C}=\text{O} \xrightarrow[\substack{\text{Pyruvic de-}\\ \text{carboxylase}}]{(11)} & \text{CHO} + \text{DPNH} \underset{\substack{\text{Alcohol de-}\\ \text{hydrogenase}}}{\overset{(12)}{\rightleftharpoons}} & \text{CH}_2\text{OH} + \text{DPN} \\
| & | & | \\
\text{CH}_3 & \text{CH}_3 & \text{CH}_3 \\
\text{Pyruvic acid} & \text{Acetaldehyde} & \text{Ethanol}
\end{array}
$$

These two reactions are of course well known as the final steps in yeast fermentation and are sometimes included as part of glycolysis.

The second fate of pyruvate is reduction to lactate by a DPNH-linked lactic dehydrogenase (Reaction 13):

$$
\begin{array}{c}
\text{COOH} \\
|\\
\text{C=O} \\
|\\
\text{CH}_3 \\
\text{Pyruvic acid}
\end{array}
+ \text{DPNH}
\underset{\text{Lactic dehydrogenase}}{\rightleftharpoons}
\begin{array}{c}
\text{COOH} \\
|\\
\text{CHOH} \\
|\\
\text{CH}_3 \\
\text{Lactic acid}
\end{array}
+ \text{DPN} \quad (13)
$$

During pyruvate conversion to either lactate or alcohol an equimolar amount of DPNH is consumed. Thus, if all of the pyruvate formed in glycolysis were reduced to one of these products, a precise balance would be struck between this reductive step and the oxidative step of glycolysis, in which 1 mole of DPNH is produced per mole of pyruvate.

A self-contained system (Figure 2) would result which would be analogous either to yeast fermentation or lactate production in muscle, and the over-all reaction would thus become

$$
\text{Hexose} + 2\text{iP} + 2\text{ADP}
\begin{array}{l}
\nearrow 2 \text{ Ethyl alcohol} + 2\text{CO}_2 + 2\text{ATP} \\
\\
\searrow 2 \text{ Lactate} + 2\text{ATP}
\end{array}
$$

EVIDENCE FOR THE OPERATION OF THE EMP GLYCOLYTIC SEQUENCE

In extracts. In much of the preliminary work leading to the separation of the individual enzymes mentioned above, it was clear that parts of the sequence were operating, and the anticipated inhibitory effects of iodoacetate and fluoride were observed. Further, it has long been known (Neuberg and Gottschalk, 1925) that ground peas and other materials are able to induce the formation of detectable amounts of ethanol from sugars. The availability of appropriate phosphorylated intermediates and cofactors made possible more convincing experiments in the 1940's (see James, 1953, Chapter VI).

Water extracts or acetone powders prepared from plant

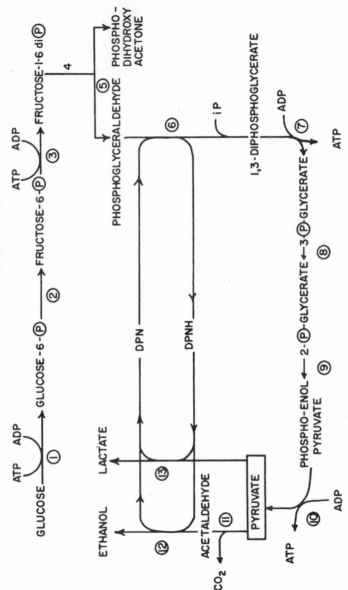

FIGURE 2.—Reactions of the Embden-Meyerhof-Parnas sequence.

materials are incapable of inducing pyruvate oxidation because the delicate mitochondrial apparatus is destroyed. The pyruvic decarboxylase and alcohol dehydrogenase, however, are retained in a sufficiently active condition so that pyruvate does not usually accumulate in such systems but is converted (Reactions 11 and 12) to alcohol, even though air is present. However, James, James, and Bunting (1941) were able to show that pyruvate was produced from fructose diphosphate in barley-leaf extracts. In his detailed investigation of the glycolytic reactions, Stumpf (1950) showed that arsenate stimulated CO_2 production from fructose diphosphate by a pea-seed extract; it was clear from inhibitor experiments that the glycolytic pathway was being followed and that the CO_2 arose from pyruvate.

Although these qualitative demonstrations are strictly in accord with the reactions outlined above, a recent contribution from Hatch and Turner (1958) has added a completely satisfying quantitative element which establishes beyond doubt that we are on safe ground in supposing that the various individual reactions do occur in a closely knit sequence. These authors used a resuspended ammonium sulfate precipitate from a pea-seed extract. When this was fortified with appropriate nucleotides and Mg^{++}, a *quantitative* conversion of hexose (and of starch or hexose phosphates) to CO_2 and ethanol was brought about (Table I). In addition it was shown that other requirements of the over-all equation were met. ATP synthesis was induced, and the yield approached the theoretical, i.e., 2 moles ATP per mole CO_2 or alcohol. It was established that DPN was undergoing cyclic oxidation and reduction and that fluoride and iodoacetate almost completely inhibited the process.

In vivo. Although it is now certain that the EMP glycolytic sequence is important in the aerobic breakdown of carbohydrates in plant tissues, the clearest proof of its operation has come from experiments in the absence of O_2. Under these conditions the pyruvate is converted to ethanol or occasionally lactate (e.g., Barker and El Saifi, 1952). However, the theoretical production of equimolar amounts of ethanol and CO_2

TABLE I

QUANTITATIVE GLYCOLYSIS BY AN ENZYME SYSTEM FROM PEAS[*]

(HATCH AND TURNER, 1958)

SUBSTRATE ADDED		PRODUCT RECOVERED (MICROMOLES)		
		CO_2	Ethanol	Inorganic P
21 micromoles fructose + 2.5 micro-	Calc.	47	47	5.0
moles fructose-1,6-diP	Found	40	41	5.7
25.2 micromoles glucose-1-P	Calc.	50.4	50.4	25.2
	Found	46	49	23.4
25 micromoles fructose-1,6-diP	Calc.	50	50	50
	Found	41	44	43.0

* The reaction mixtures contained ATP, DPN, and Mg^{++} in phosphate buffer in addition to enzyme and the substrates as shown.

is not always observed (Kostychev, 1927); see James (1953) or Thomas (1957) for a review. Some of the low values for alcohol/CO_2 ratios were obtained after many hours without oxygen, but it is clear that even in shorter periods an excess of CO_2 might be produced from decarboxylations not directly related to alcohol production (Phillips, 1947). Thus the rate of CO_2 evolution in N_2 cannot be taken as a sure indication of the rate of alcohol production. Nevertheless, a sufficient number of tissues have provided values close to 1 to make it likely that alcohol and CO_2 are being produced according to Reactions 1–12; the divergent values are due no doubt to superimposed and as yet incompletely characterized reactions. The recent demonstration of James and Ritchie (1955) is a comforting one (Table II). These authors showed that in carrot tissue, for which an alcohol/CO_2 ratio close to unity was already known, sugar loss from the tissue during a period in N_2 was entirely accounted for by the alcohol and CO_2 produced. The quantitative requirements of the Gay-Lussac equation,

$$C_6H_{12}O_6 \rightarrow 2C_2H_5OH + 2CO_2 ,$$

were precisely met (Table II).

Observations with labeled glucose are pertinent here. Bee-

TABLE II
ANAEROBIC SUGAR UTILIZATION IN CARROTS*
(JAMES AND RITCHIE, 1954)

	Initial Sugar	Final Sugar	Sugar Utilized	Alcohol Formed	CO_2 Released
A	1.812	1.434	0.378	0.220	0.115
B	1.054	0.426	0.628	0.405	0.203

* All of the figures are in g carbon/100 g/f.wt. carrot tissue. A and B are separate experiments, and the values shown are the means of 6 determinations.

vers and Gibbs (1954a) provided glucose-1-C^{14} to corn root tips and measured the appearance of radioactivity in the CO_2 and in the individual carbons of the alcohol which was recovered. It was found that, as predicted from the EMP sequence of reactions,

$$
\begin{array}{cccccc}
1 & 2 & 3 & 4 & 5 & 6 \\
C\!-\!C\!-\!C\!-\!C\!-\!C\!-\!C
\end{array} \qquad \text{Glucose}
$$

$$
\begin{array}{cccccc}
1 & 2 & 3 & 4 & 5 & 6 \\
C\!-\!C\!-\!C\rightleftharpoons C\!-\!C\!-\!C
\end{array} \qquad \downarrow \quad \text{Triose}
$$

$$
\begin{array}{ccc}
1,6 & 2,5 & 3,4 \\
CH_3\!-\!\underset{\underset{O}{\|}}{C}\!-\!COOH
\end{array} \qquad \downarrow \quad \text{Pyruvate}
$$

$$
\begin{array}{ccc}
1,6 & 2,5 & 3,4 \\
CH_3\!-\! CH_2OH & + & CO_2
\end{array} \qquad \downarrow \quad \text{Ethanol} + CO_2
$$

the CO_2 produced was nonradioactive, and only the CH_3 group of the alcohol contained C^{14}. The CO_2 was radioactive when glucose-3,4-C^{14} was the substrate, and only the carbinol carbon of ethanol contained C^{14} when glucose-2-C^{14} was the substrate.

Evidence from inhibitor experiments can also be adduced to support the view that the anaerobic breakdown of glucose occurs by the EMP glycolysis sequence. Thus iodoacetate and fluoride are known to curtail the anaerobic production of CO_2 by a variety of plant tissues (e.g., Tang et al., 1956).

Finally, the detection of small amounts of acetaldehyde in anaerobic experiments and its reduction to ethanol by intact tissues (Fidler, 1937) may be quoted as supporting the view that it is the precursor of ethanol, as required by Reaction 12.

Whereas under N_2 the production of ethanol and CO_2 shows that pyruvate was a precursor, the final product in air gives no such clue as to its origin. It is well established of course that the glycolytic enzymes can operate in air, but the sharp cutoff in the production of ethanol which occurs when most tissues are provided with air was reasonably ascribed at one time to the stopping of glycolysis. It is now clear that aerobic events do in fact play a role in regulating the *rate* of glycolysis (p. 150), but it is also clear that pyruvate production by glycolysis occurs in air and that it is only the production of ethanol which is drastically interfered with. The evidence may be summarized as follows.

a. The established inhibitors of glycolytic enzymes, iodoacetate and fluoride, inhibit CO_2 output and O_2 uptake at levels close to those which likewise inhibit fermentation.

b. Pyruvate can to some extent restore the respiration of some tissues inhibited by fluoride (Laties, 1949) and may itself stimulate O_2 uptake (e.g., James and Hora, 1940; Laties, 1949; Tang *et al.*, 1956; and Ramshorn, 1957b). A frequent response to the addition of pyruvate in substrate amounts is an increased R.Q. and the production of ethanol, even though air is present (Ramshorn, 1957b; Gentile and Naylor, 1956).

c. The rates of appearance of the individual carbons of glucose in the respired CO_2 are consistent in some tissues with the production of pyruvate as an intermediate, i.e., carbons 3 and 4 appear first, followed by C2 + C5 and then by C1 + C6.

d. When pyruvate is provided in small amounts, it is completely utilized in oxidative reactions. None of it is diverted to ethanol, and the rates of appearance of its individual carbons as CO_2 correspond closely with those of the equivalent carbons of glucose (Chapter 3).

e. Arsenite, which blocks the initial steps in the aerobic removal of pyruvate, induces the *aerobic* formation of

TABLE III

Location of C^{14} in Ethanol Produced during Arsenite-Induced Aerobic
Fermentation in Corn Root Tips (Beevers and Gibbs, 1954a)

Substrate	Percentage of C^{14} in Ethanol	
	In CH_2OH	In CH_3
Glucose-1-C^{14}	2.5	97.5
Glucose-2-C^{14}	97.2	2.8
Glucose-3,4-C^{14}	0	0

ethanol and CO_2 (Beevers and Gibbs, 1954a; ap Rees and Beevers, 1960a). This indicates again that the glycolytic reactions occur in air, and, when specifically labeled glucoses were provided, the distribution of C^{14} in the ethanol showed that it had arisen from the predicted carbons of glucose (Table III). That is to say, carbon 1 of glucose was confined to the methyl group of the ethanol, and carbon 2 of glucose to the carbinol carbon; carbons 3 and 4 did not appear in the ethanol but were found in the respiratory CO_2 (Table III).

f. Other inhibitors, such as malonate, fluoroacetate, and CO_2, which interfere with the later steps in pyruvate oxidation, and inhibitors of terminal electron transfer induce aerobic fermentation (Tables IV, X).

g. 2,4-Dinitrophenol (DNP) at appropriate concentrations stimulates O_2 consumption but stimulates CO_2 output even more (Newcomb, 1950; Beevers, 1953). This extra CO_2 is accompanied by the production of ethanol and acetaldehyde. DNP apparently induces aerobic fermentation because it (indirectly) stimulates glycolysis, and the excess pyruvate is decarboxylated (p. 153).

h. Glycerol is utilized by some tissues, in a fashion which is consistent with its conversion to phosphoglycerate and pyruvate (Stumpf, 1955; Beevers, 1956b). Under appropriate conditions its carbon too can be diverted to ethanol (Beevers, 1956b).

i. The finding that ethanol production is progressively reduced in plant tissues as the O_2 content of the gas is in-

TABLE IV

Effect of KCN, Low O_2, and CO on Respiration, and Respiration Quotient of Various Pollens (Okunuki, 1939)

	CONTROL		0.001 M KCN		95% N_2 + 5% O_2		95% CO + 5% O_2	
	$\dfrac{Q\ CO_2}{Q\ O_2}$	R.Q.	$\dfrac{Q\ CO_2}{Q\ O_2}$	R.Q.	$\dfrac{Q\ CO_2}{Q\ O_2}$	R.Q.	$\dfrac{Q\ CO_2}{Q\ O_2}$	R.Q.
Lilium longiflorum	$\dfrac{9.81}{9.70}$	1.01	$\dfrac{10.83}{4.50}$	2.41	$\dfrac{9.63}{7.78}$	1.24	$\dfrac{12.54}{5.42}$	2.31
Camellia japonica	$\dfrac{6.88}{6.74}$	1.02	$\dfrac{7.60}{0.57}$	13.3	$\dfrac{12.69}{8.35}$	1.52	$\dfrac{9.56}{1.66}$	5.76
Camellia sansangua	$\dfrac{4.49}{4.38}$	1.03	$\dfrac{6.08}{1.95}$	3.12	$\dfrac{2.08}{1.97}$	1.06	$\dfrac{2.13}{0.70}$	3.04

creased from zero is consistent with an increasing diversion of pyruvate away from ethanol production and into oxidative channels. We may note that, in some tissues, very high levels of O_2 may be required for a complete suppression of ethanol production (Betz, 1957, 1958; Ramshorn, 1957a); aerobic fermentation which cannot be ascribed to a restriction in O_2 supply by an impermeable structure occurs in air in some meristems (Ruhland and Ramshorn, 1938) and in aging fruits.

It will be seen that, although all of the foregoing is consistent with the production of pyruvate by the EMP pathway as an essential part of respiration in air, the possible production of pyruvate by a somewhat different pathway, not involving aldolase, is not ruled out. The operation of such a sequence and its significance are discussed in the next section.

THE PENTOSE PHOSPHATE PATHWAY

The early work of Dickens (1938a,b) and Warburg *et al.* (1935) which showed the existence of enzymes bringing about a direct oxidation of glucose-6-phosphate came to its flowering in the early 1950's. It was at this time, particularly through the efforts of Horecker (see Horecker and Mehler, 1955) and

Racker (1954), that the subsequent reactions were elucidated and the pentose phosphate pathway, as shown in Figure 3, was established.

The first indications that such an alternative pathway of glucose breakdown might play a role in plant metabolism came from two types of observations. First, the reports from Vennesland's (Anderson *et al.*, 1952; Barnett *et al.*, 1953), Axelrod's (Axelrod and Bandurski, 1952; Axelrod *et al.*, 1953), and Gibbs's groups (Gibbs, 1952) made it clear that glucose-6-phosphate dehydrogenase, or Zwischenferment (Catalyzing Reaction 1), was widespread in plant materials:

$$\text{Glucose-6-phosphate} + \text{TPN} \rightarrow$$
$$\text{6-Phosphogluconate} + \text{TPNH} + \text{H}^+ \quad (1)$$

TPNH-glutathione reductase was present in many extracts, and the oxidation was thus linked to glutathione reduction. Gibbs (1954) showed that when glucose-6-phosphate, 6-phosphogluconate, or ribose-5-phosphate was added to soluble pea extracts in the presence of TPN an active uptake of O_2 occurred. Glucose-6-phosphate oxidation was linked to O_2 by a cyanide-stable oxidase. The product of glucose-6-phosphate oxidation, 6-phosphogluconate, did not accumulate in the enzyme experiments because it was attacked by another TPN-linked dehydrogenase (6-phosphogluconate dehydrogenase), which had been shown to be present in a variety of tissues by the authors mentioned above. The products of the reaction were a pentose phosphate, CO_2, and TPNH (Reaction 2) (see also the experiments of Clayton, 1959, on tobacco):

$$\text{6-Phosphogluconate} + \text{TPN} \rightarrow$$
$$\text{Ribulose-5-phosphate} + CO_2 + \text{TPNH} \quad (2)$$

The subsequent stages of the pentose phosphate pathway consist of rearrangements in which the carbons of the C-5 units produced in Reaction 2 are recombined to produce hexose and triose units. This sequence involves the participation of C-7, C-4, and C-3 phosphorylated sugars, and, as indicated below, the requisite enzymes have been found in plant materials. The formation of hexose from pentose units

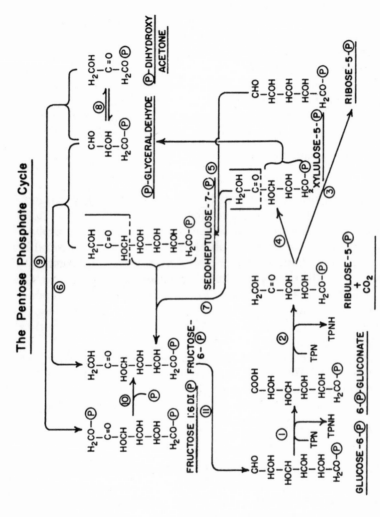

FIGURE 3.—Reactions of the pentose phosphate sequence.

by reactions in which sedoheptulose and triose phosphates were intermediates was neatly demonstrated in spinach extracts by Axelrod *et al.* (1953). Gibbs and Horecker (1954) were able to isolate radioactive glucose phosphate from pea preparations which had been provided with specifically labeled pentose phosphates. Their demonstration that the location of C^{14} in the hexose was close to that predicted was crucial for the view that the reactions were occurring largely as indicated in Figure 3.

It is now clear that a variety of enzymes exist which bring about isomeric changes in the pentose phosphates and that their action is a necessary prerequisite to pentose breakdown. One of these is phosphoriboisomerase, which brings about Reaction 3:

$$
\begin{array}{ccc}
\text{CHO} & \text{CH}_2\text{OH} & \text{CH}_2\text{OH} \\
| & | & | \\
\text{HCOH} & \text{C}{=}\text{O} & \text{C}{=}\text{O} \\
| \quad\quad (3) & | \quad\quad (4) & | \\
\text{HCOH} \rightleftharpoons & \text{HCOH} \rightleftharpoons & \text{OHCH} \\
| & | & | \\
\text{HCOH} & \text{HCOH} & \text{HCOH} \\
| & | & | \\
\text{CH}_2\text{O(P)} & \text{CH}_2\text{O(P)} & \text{CH}_2\text{O(P)} \\
\text{Ribose-5-phosphate} & \text{Ribulose-5-phosphate} & \text{Xylulose-5-phosphate}
\end{array}
$$

We may note that this reaction is analogous to those brought about by the hexose phosphate and triose phosphate isomerases. However, it is brought about by a specific enzyme which was obtained in a highly purified form from spinach leaves by Axelrod and Jang (1954). In addition, epimeric changes round carbon-3 are brought about by pentulose phosphate epimerase. Ribulose-5-phosphate is thus converted into xylulose-5-phosphate (Reaction 4). The pentose phosphate pool is seen to be a heterogeneous one.

The actual cleavage of a C-5 unit is brought about by transketolase. This enzyme has also been highly purified from spinach leaves (Horecker *et al.*, 1953). In the presence of thiamine pyrophosphate (TPP) and Mg^{++} ions it brings about the transfer of carbons 1 and 2 from xylulose-5-phosphate to ribose-5-phosphate. The products are sedoheptulose phosphate and triose phosphate (Reaction 5):

Xylulose-5-phosphate $\qquad$ Ribose-5-phosphate
  (C$_2$ donor)   (C$_2$ acceptor)   (5)
3-Phosphoglyceraldehyde $\qquad$ Sedoheptulose-7-phosphate

The action of transketolase is not limited to the transfer indicated in Reaction 5. A C-2 unit can be transferred from a variety of ketoses, with the appropriate configuration at C-3, to a variety of acceptor aldoses. Fructose-6-phosphate, L-erythulose, and sedoheptulose phosphate are examples of other C-2 donors, and D-(or L-)glyceraldehyde-3-phosphate, glycolaldehyde, and erythrose-4-phosphate are other acceptors.

The sedoheptulose produced in Reaction 5 is subsequently attacked by transaldolase, another TPP-requiring enzyme, which transfers a C-3 unit (dihydroxyacetone phosphate) to phosphoglyceraldehyde (Reaction 6):

Sedoheptulose-7-phosphate $\qquad$ 3-Phosphoglyceraldehyde
  (C$_3$ donor)   (C$_3$ acceptor)   (6)
Erythrose-4-phosphate $\qquad$ Fructose-6-phosphate

As with the transketolase enzyme, other substances may fill the roles of donor and acceptor, and the C-3 unit which is transferred does not appear free in the reaction mixture; it is presumed to be bound to enzyme or coenzyme during the reaction.

Erythrose-4-phosphate produced in ·Reaction 6 is an acceptor in the transketolase reaction, and with xylulose-5-phosphate acting as the C-2 donor the products are fructose-6-phosphate and glyceraldehyde-3-phosphate (Reaction 7):

Xylulose-5-phosphate $\qquad$ Erythrose-4-phosphate
  (C$_2$ donor)   (C$_2$ acceptor)   (7)
Glyceraldehyde-3-phosphate $\qquad$ Fructose-6-phosphate

The net result of Reactions 5, 6, and 7 is that 3 moles of pentose phosphate are converted into 2 moles of hexose phosphate and 1 of triose phosphate. Thus, if 6 moles of glucose-

6-phosphate enter the pentose phosphate sequence, they give rise to 6 moles of CO_2 (derived exclusively from C-1), 12 moles of TPNH, 4 moles of hexose phosphate, and 2 moles of triose phosphate. In the presence of triose phosphate isomerase (Reaction 8) and aldolase (Reaction 9) the two triose phosphates may combine to give rise to a further hexose unit, and thus the reactions may be drawn in a cycle, in which 6 moles of hexose phosphate enter and give rise to 5 of hexose phosphate and 6 of CO_2. Such a sequence is shown in Figure 4. The carbon atoms are numbered so that their origin may be traced.

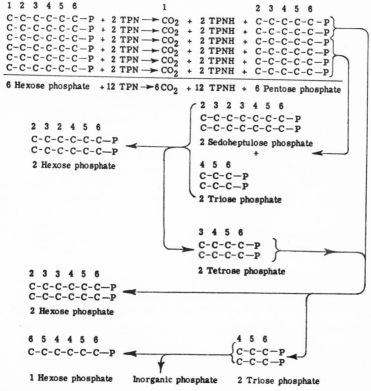

FIGURE 4.—Schematic representation of the passage of 6 molecules of hexose phosphate through the pentose phosphate cycle. The numbers refer to the positions of the carbons in the original hexose. (Axelrod and Beevers, 1956.)

The hexose phosphate produced as a result of one turn of the cycle would be expected to mix with the native hexose pool and may thus traverse the circuit several times. It should be emphasized that a likely alternative fate for the triose phosphate produced in Reactions 5 and 7 is entry into the glycolytic sequence and conversion to pyruvate.

Plant materials have not been systematically investigated for the presence of all of the enzymes of the pentose phosphate pathway. However, the widespread occurrence of the oxidative enzymes in plants where they have been sought, the demonstration of the complete sequence in some plant extracts, and the isolation of transketolase, transaldolase, and the requisite isomerases in pure form sustain the view that the pentose phosphate pathway must be considered, along with other known pathways, as a component of the carbohydrate breakdown.

THE PENTOSE PHOSPHATE PATHWAY *in vivo*

Before the reactions subsequent to pentose formation were elucidated, it was customary to regard the so-called "direct oxidation" of glucose-6-phosphate as the probable source of intact pentose units in larger molecules in the cell. It is now clear, however, that the C-5 units produced in the pentose phosphate sequence are broken down. Furthermore, other mechanisms (decarboxylation at C-6 and aldol condensation of C_2 and C_3 units) now appear to be more important in generating those C-5 units which are destined for structural roles in the plant.

The significance of the pathway may therefore be sought in the respiratory breakdown of glucose-6-phosphate. In this role the pentose phosphate pathway may be regarded as a diversion of hexose units from the conventional glycolytic pathway—a bypass, that is to say, around the aldolase step on the way from hexose to pyruvate. Alternatively, if the circuit is closed by conversion of the triose phosphate to hexose, the cycle is a self-contained unit by which glucose-6-phosphate may be completely oxidized. If TPNH oxidation were coupled to ATP generation, the pathway would be energetically efficient. However, other drains on TPNH, such as oxidation by soluble oxidase systems and utilization in important reductive events in the cell, also merit consideration.

Some tissues, such as pea internodes and coleoptiles, are known to contain the principal enzymes of both EMP and pentose phosphate pathways (Gibbs et al., 1955; Gibbs and Earl, 1959). The present indications are that all of these enzymes reside naturally in the soluble phase of the protoplasm, although an association of the dehydrogenases of the pentose phosphate pathway with particles has recently been found in peas (Marrè, personal communication). The question of what determines the extent of diversion of glucose-6-phosphate to the pentose phosphate pathway becomes a critical one, since it is apparently not simply a matter of enzyme competition for a mutual substrate. At present, two aspects of control which may be considered are:

a. the rate of reoxidation of TPNH, which might well limit diversion of glucose through the pentose phosphate sequence; and

b. inhibitory effects of intermediates of the pentose phosphate sequence (6-phosphogluconate, erythrose-4-phosphate) on the glucose-6-phosphate isomerase.

The evidence for the participation of the pentose phosphate pathway in plant metabolism has come almost entirely from tracer experiments and may be summarized as follows.

The presence of C_3, C_4, C_5, C_6, and C_7 sugar phosphates in plants. The participation of these compounds in the metabolism of leaves became clear from work with $C^{14}O_2$ on photosynthesis (Benson et al., 1952). The fact that C_5 and C_7 sugars are actively metabolized in the dark and by nongreen plant tissues has been more recently established. For example, Krotkov et al. (1955) demonstrated the interconvertibility of hexoses and pentoses, and Tolbert and Zill (1954), using sedoheptulose-U-C^{14} isolated from *Sedum,* showed that its carbon could be converted in the dark to a variety of compounds including amino acids and C_4, C_5, and C_6 sugars.

The fates of individual carbons of pentoses and sedoheptu-

lose in feeding experiments. The operation of the pentose phosphate cycle was unmistakably shown by Neish and his colleagues in a brilliant series of experiments which were designed to elucidate the origin of cell-wall components (Altermatt and Neish, 1956; Brown and Neish, 1954; and Neish, 1955). These authors observed that D-xylose-1-C^{14} and D-ribose-1-C^{14} were converted into hexose units in which C-1 of the xylose became C_1 and C_3 of the hexose unit in an approximately $2:1$ ratio. This is the distribution predicted by Figure 4. Ginsburg and Hassid (1956), also using wheat seedlings, isolated sucrose-C^{14} which had been produced from D-xylose-1-C^{14}, and here too it was clear that the transaldolase and transketolase reactions (Figure 3) had contributed to the observed distribution of C^{14} within the hexose units. Neish (1955) also demonstrated that carbon from sedoheptulose-2-C^{14} appeared both in pentose and hexose units in a fashion which would have been predicted from Figure 3.

The ability of intermediates of the pentose phosphate pathway (gluconate, pentose, sedoheptulose) to act as respiratory substrates, in a way predicted from Figure 4. It was clear from the work mentioned above that carbon from pentoses and sedoheptulose appeared in the respired CO_2. Beevers (1956a) tested the ability of a variety of plant tissues to use pentose, gluconate, and sedoheptulose as respiratory substrates.

Carbon from D-ribose-1-C^{14} and D-xylose-1-C^{14} was converted to CO_2 by corn and pea tissues, both in air and in N_2. The distribution of C^{14} in the ethanol and CO_2 produced either anaerobically, or aerobically in the presence of arsenite, showed that the C^{14} in the precursor pyruvate was confined to carbons 1 and 3 in roughly $1:2$ ratio. This is the distribution expected if the pentose had undergone complete conversion to hexose in the pentose phosphate cycle (Figure 4) and the hexose had then been subject to breakdown by the EMP sequence. Sedoheptulose-U-C^{14} was also utilized in air and N_2. Both carbon atoms of the ethanol were labeled. The CO_2 produced from specifically labeled gluconates was initially very much higher in C-1 than in C-2 or C-6. The fact that the first reaction of gluconate metabolism in the pentose phosphate pathway is an oxidative decarboxylation explains why, in contrast to sedoheptulose and pentose, the utilization of gluconate in N_2 was very much lower than that in air. However, small amounts of ethanol and CO_2 were produced from gluconate, and again the distribution of C^{14} was consistent with the conversion of gluconate to pentose by the pentose phosphate pathway and subsequent conversion to ethanol and CO_2 via conventional glycolysis.

Thus it is clear that at least some plant cells have the equipment for carrying out the reactions of the pentose phosphate pathway and that it can be shown to be functional *in vivo*.

ATTEMPTS TO ASSESS THE IMPORTANCE OF THE PENTOSE PHOSPHATE PATHWAY IN THE RESPIRATORY BREAKDOWN OF GLUCOSE

If a given glucose molecule is completely respired, by whatever pathway, all of its individual carbons will eventually appear as CO_2. But, depending on which pathway is actually taken, certain carbon atoms in the molecule will make an earlier appearance than others in the CO_2, and as the remaining fragments of the molecule complete the various reactions and pass through pools of intermediates, the rest of the carbons will appear in sequence.

The important difference in this respect between the two pathways for which we have evidence is the following. For those glucose molecules which are broken down exclusively by the EMP sequence (in which a split to two equivalent pyruvate molecules occurs), the first carbons to appear in CO_2 would be those from positions 3 and 4. Carbons 2 and 5 would appear only after a complete circuit of the TCA cycle by the remaining acetyl unit. Carbons 1 and 6 would appear last, and indistinguishably, after yet further circuits (Chapter 3).

By contrast, C-1 is the first carbon to appear from those glucose molecules entering the pentose phosphate sequence, and it is, moreover, unaccompanied by C-6. The rate of conversion of C-6 to CO_2 would be determined by whether the trioses produced in the pentose phosphate pathway were converted to pyruvate or were recycled; in either event its appearance, relative to that of C-1, would be considerably delayed. Less striking but predictable differences in the rates of appearance of the other carbons of glucose would be expected, depending on which pathway was taken.

For the moment it is sufficient to note that valuable information can be obtained by comparing the radioactivity of the early CO_2 produced from equal samples of tissue, one supplied with glucose-1-C^{14} and the other with glucose-6-C^{14}. This so-called "C_6/C_1 ratio" was introduced initially by Bloom and Stetten (1953) as a means of demonstrating the participation of the pentose phosphate pathway in animal tissues. They suggested further that, since the maximum amount of C-1 which could have arisen from the EMP pathway was an amount equal to the fraction of C-6 recovered, the C_6/C_1 ratio provided directly a fraction showing the maximum participation of the EMP pathway in the respiration of glucose.

Some of the assumptions recognized and implied in this evaluation have since been shown not to hold universally. Of particular importance is the fact that drainage of some intermediates from the TCA cycle into cellular constituents occurs, and this precludes the appearance of certain carbons as CO_2. This differential effect on the carbons of glucose may cause the final yield from C-3 and C-4 to be considerably greater than that from carbons 1, 2, 5, and 6. The EMP sequence may be underestimated by the extent to which equal amounts of C-1 and C-6 are retained.

As a means of estimating the pathways of total glucose consumption, then, the C_6/C_1 ratio does not give an unequivocal result. What is definitely shown by this ratio is the relative contributions of the EMP and pentose phosphate pathways to the release of C-1 of the supplied glucose as CO_2. At present a ratio of unity would be consistent with (but would not prove) the proposition that breakdown was entirely by the EMP sequence, whereas a ratio of less than 1 would show that some unknown fraction of the glucose was diverted to the pentose phosphate pathway.

Various plant materials have been examined by this method, and the great majority yielded ratios much less than 1 (Beevers and Gibbs, 1954b)—clear evidence of the participation of the pentose phosphate sequence in the respiration of the supplied glucose. In general, older aerial parts yielded lower ratios, and meristematic tissues were the only ones from which release of carbons 1 and 6 was equal in short-term experiments (Gibbs and Beevers, 1955). For these tissues independent evidence was provided which confirmed that glucose breakdown was predominantly by the EMP sequence. We may note that in mammals, muscle tissue, which is usually the bulkiest, shows no evidence of the participation of the pentose phosphate sequence by Bloom and Stetten's method. In contrast to the situation in plants, it seems to be of limited importance and is confined to specialized organs.

Subsequent work with other plant tissues (Daly et al., 1957; Shaw and Samborski, 1957; Shaw et al., 1958; Doyle and Wang, 1958; and Barbour et al., 1958) has further strengthened the view that diversion of glucose-6-phosphate through the pentose phosphate pathway occurs generally. Some of these authors have been interested in the effects of infection; striking decreases in the ratio, indicating an increased traffic through the pentose phosphate pathway, result from invasion by the pathogens which were studied. Humphreys and Dugger (1957a,b) have presented evidence from experiments with pea seedlings that the extra respiration elicited in this tissue by 2,4-D has a strong pentose phosphate pathway component.

In extensive work with carrot tissues (ap Rees and Beevers, 1960b), it was shown that the participation of the pentose phosphate pathway, as indicated by the C_6/C_1 ratio, increases during the respiratory rise elicited by washing for several hours. Comparable data have been obtained for potato. The ratio is furthermore subject to experimental modification by the addition of substances which can be expected to speed up or slow down partial reactions of the individual sequences (ap Rees and Beevers, 1960a). Thus arsenite, which blocks pyruvate utilization, increases the relative contribution of

C-1 to the CO_2. DNP, which indirectly induces an increased rate of glycolysis in this tissue, increases the contribution of C-6 and brings the ratio closer to 1 (see also Shaw and Samborski, 1957, and Daly *et al.*, 1957). Methylene blue, which facilitates TPNH oxidation, also induces a significantly greater contribution of C-1. These results are uniformly consistent with the concept that, in the untreated tissues, both pathways of glucose breakdown participate and that the extent of this participation is in some way internally regulated.

In other experiments the progressive release of C-1 and C-6 has been followed over longer periods. It became clear from these that, although the early phase of preponderance of C-1 in the CO_2 might be succeeded by one in which C-6 release exceeds that of C-1, the amount of C-6 eventually recovered was never equal to that of C-1, even in the longest experiments. Such an equality should be demonstrated for a valid application of the C_6/C_1 ratio as described by Bloom and Stetten (see discussion in Axelrod and Beevers, 1956).

One possible explanation of the "retention" of C-6 which, it will be realized, would lead to an overestimation of the pentose phosphate pathway is that the C-5 unit either accumulates or is drained off into cellular constituents such as pentosans. This possibility was definitely ruled out in the carrot tissue referred to above; the excess of C-6 which was retained was entirely accounted for in organic acids, amino acids, and protein components. It was clear that the C-5 unit corresponding to the C-1 lost initially as CO_2 was further metabolized; its carbon appeared in pyruvate and the various compounds derived from it.

The retention of individual carbons of the glucose is clearly brought out in additional experiments in which release of $C^{14}O_2$ from glucose specifically labeled in 1, 2, 3, 4, and 6 positions was measured. Valuable data have also been provided for pepper fruit and tomato by the Oregon group (Doyle and Wang, 1958; Barbour *et al.*, 1958). The progress curves show clearly that the release of C-1 might be more than twice as rapid as that of C-6 (C_6/C_1 less than 0.5) and yet the release of C-3 and C-4 might be as high as, or even exceed,

TABLE V

CONTRIBUTION OF INDIVIDUAL CARBONS OF GLUCOSE TO RESPIRED CO_2

TISSUE AND TIME (HR.)	% OF RESPIRED CO_2 FROM INDIVIDUAL CARBONS						AUTHORS
	1	2	3	4	5 (Calc.)	6	
Corn root tip (6)	11	8	32	32	8	10	Butt and Beevers, 1960
Tomato fruit (2)	16	6	32	32	6	7	Barbour et al., 1958
Pepper fruit (10)	20	13	24	24	13	7	Doyle and Wang, 1958
Fresh carrot slices (6)	19	10	27	27	10	6	ap Rees and Beevers, 1960
Washed carrot slices (3)	28	12	20	20	12	9	ap Rees and Beevers, 1960
Washed potato slices (6)	25	15	18	18	15	9	ap Rees and Beevers, 1960

that of C-1 (Table V). Release of C-3 and C-4 can occur by reactions other than the oxidative decarboxylation of pyruvate, but the figures probably represent to a large degree this reaction on pyruvate generated by the EMP sequence. The fact that the release of C-2 and C-6 corresponding to carbons 2 and 3 of the pyruvate lags so far behind, and may not in fact appear at all during the experiments, emphasizes that C-6 release as CO_2 is an incomplete indication of the amount of pyruvate produced by the EMP sequence in these tissues. Results of pyruvate feeding experiments (Neal and Beevers, 1960; ap Rees and Beevers, 1960b) confirm this view.

Other methods of estimating precisely the contributions of the pathways to total glucose utilization have been proposed and evaluated (e.g., Barbour et al., 1958; Shaw and Samborski, 1957). Each of these involves assumptions, and none seems to be generally acceptable or applicable. In some of these methods the fate of the C-5 unit is not considered and it is assumed that the only carbon to appear from the pentose phosphate pathway is the original C-1 of the glucose, whereas it is quite clear that any glucose resynthesized by the pentose phosphate pathway would now have a different carbon atom in position 1 and this would be released as CO_2 when the glucose molecule re-entered the sequence. A further complication is that pyruvate produced from triose drained from succeeding cycles of the pentose phosphate sequence would have a changing complement of the original glucose carbons. This introduces further hazards into calculations of the importance of the alternate sequences (ap Rees and Beevers, 1960a).

Thus, although the contribution cannot be precisely estimated, the present evidence shows that, in addition to the classical glycolysis sequence, breakdown via the pentose phosphate sequence plays a role in glucose dissimilation in the majority of higher plant tissues, and in some it would appear to account for at least one third of the hexose utilized (Doyle and Wang, 1958). In looking for some functional value of this diversion, several authors (see, e.g., Horecker and Hiatt, 1958; Holzer, 1959) have pointed to the possibile utility of the TPNH generated in the oxidation of glucose-6-phosphate in synthetic and reductive events. In fact, Dickens' group (see Dickens, Glock, and McLean, 1959) has emphasized that the rate of TPNH utilization may be the pacemaker reaction governing traffic through the pentose phosphate sequence. It is significant, then, that the addition of agents which might be expected to stimulate TPNH oxidation elicit a greater participation of the pentose phosphate reactions in plant tissues (ap Rees and Beevers, 1960a; Butt and Beevers, 1960). The general participation of these reactions in plant materials may be due to the facility with which electrons from TPNH are transferred to O_2, possibly by soluble enzymes, or to internal H-accepting systems by appropriate dehydrogenases (p. 182).

REFERENCES

ALTERMATT, H. A., and NEISH, A. C. Can. J. Biochem. Physiol. 34, 405 (1956).
ANDERSON, D. G., STAFFORD, H. A., CONN, E. E., and VENNESLAND, B. Plant Physiol. 27, 675 (1952).
AP REES, T., and BEEVERS, H. Plant Physiol. 35, 830 (1960a).
AP REES, T., and BEEVERS, H. Plant Physiol. 35, 839 (1960b).
ARNON, D. I., Science 116, 635 (1952).
ARNON, D. I., ROSENBERG, L. L., and WHATLEY, F. R. Nature 173, 1132 (1954).
AXELROD, B., and BANDURSKI, R. S. Fed. Proc. 11, 182 (1952).

AXELROD, B., and BANDURSKI, R. S. Jour. Biol. Chem. 204, 939 (1953).
AXELROD, B., BANDURSKI, R. S., GREINER, C. M., and JANG, R. Jour. Biol. Chem. 202, 619 (1953).
AXELROD, B., and BEEVERS, H. Ann. Rev. Plant Physiol. 7, 267 (1956).
AXELROD, B., and JANG, R. Jour. Biol. Chem. 209, 847 (1954).
AXELROD, B., SALTMAN, P., BANDURSKI, R. S., and BAKER, R. S. Jour. Biol. Chem. 197, 89 (1952).
BARBOUR, R. D., BUHLER, D. R., and WANG, C. H. Plant Physiol. 33, 396 (1958).
BARKER, J., and EL SAIFI, A. F. Proc. Roy. Soc. B140, 362 (1952).
BARNETT, R. C., STAFFORD, H. A., CONN, E. E., and VENNESLAND, B. Plant Physiol. 28, 115 (1953).
BEEVERS, H. Am. Jour. Botany 40, 91 (1953).
BEEVERS, H. Plant Physiol. 31, 339 (1956a).
BEEVERS, H. Plant Physiol. 31, 440 (1956b).
BEEVERS, H., and GIBBS, M. Plant Physiol. 29, 318 (1954a).
BEEVERS, H., and GIBBS, M. Plant Physiol. 29, 322 (1954b).
BENSON, A. A., BASSHAM, J. A., CALVIN, M., HALL, A. G., HIRSCH, H. E., KAWAGUCHI, S., LYNCH, V., and TOLBERT, N. E. Jour. Biol. Chem. 196, 703 (1952).
BETZ, A. Planta 50, 122 (1957).
BETZ, A. Flora 146, 532 (1958).
BIALE, J. B., YOUNG, R. E., POPPER, C. S., and APPLEMAN, W. E. Physiol. Plant. 10, 48 (1957).
BLOOM, G., and STETTEN, D. Jour. Am. Chem. Soc. 75, 5446 (1953).
BROWN, A. S., and NEISH, A. C. Can. J. Biochem. Physiol. 32, 170 (1954).
BUTT, V. S., and BEEVERS, H. Biochem. Jour. 76, 51P (1960).
CLAYTON, R. A. Arch. Biochem. Biophys. 79, 111 (1959).
COLOWICK, S. P., and KAPLAN, N. O. (eds.) Methods in Enzymology, Academic Press, New York (1955).
DALY, J. M., SAYRE, R. M., and PAZUR, J. H. Plant Physiol. 32, 44 (1957).
DICKENS, F. Biochem. Jour. 32, 1626 (1938a).
DICKENS, F. Biochem. Jour. 32, 1645 (1938b).
DICKENS, F., GLOCK, G. E., and McLEAN, P., in Ciba Symposium, Regulation of Cell Metabolism (G. E. W. WOLSTENHOLME and C. M. O'CONNOR, eds.), Churchill, London (1959).
DOYLE, W. P., and WANG, G. H. Can. J. Botany 36, 483 (1958).
FIDLER, J. C. Ann. Rept. Food Investigation London, p. 124 (1937).
GENTILE, A. C., and NAYLOR, A. W. Arch. Biochem. Biophys. 58, 270 (1956).
GIBBS, M. Nature 170, 164 (1952).
GIBBS, M. Plant Physiol. 29, 34 (1954).
GIBBS, M., in Methods in Enzymology, Vol. I (S. P. COLOWICK and N. O. KAPLAN, eds.), Academic Press, New York (1955).
GIBBS, M., and BEEVERS, H. Plant Physiol. 30, 343 (1955).
GIBBS, M., and EARL, J. M. Plant Physiol. 34, 529 (1959).
GIBBS, M., EARL, J. M., and RITCHIE, J. L. Plant Physiol. 30, 463 (1955).
GIBBS, M., and HORECKER, B. L. Jour. Biol. Chem. 208, 813 (1954).
GINSBURG, V., and HASSID, W. Z. Jour. Biol. Chem. 223, 277 (1956).
HAGEMAN, R. H., and ARNON, D. I. Arch. Biochem. Biophys. 55, 162 (1955a).
HAGEMAN, R. H., and ARNON, D. I. Arch. Biochem. Biophys. 57, 421 (1955b).
HARDEN, A. Alcoholic Fermentation, Longmans, Green & Co., London (1923).
HATCH, M. D., and TURNER, J. F. Biochem. Jour. 69, 495 (1958).

HOLZER, H. Ann. Rev. Biochem. **28**, 171 (1959).
HORECKER, B. L., and HIATT, H. H. New England Jour. Med. **258**, 225 (1958).
HORECKER, B. L., and MEHLER, A. H. Ann. Rev. Biochem. **24**, 207 (1955).
HORECKER, B. L., SMYRNIOTIS, P. Z., and KLENOW, H. Jour. Biol. Chem. **205**, 661 (1953).
HUMPHREYS, T. E., and DUGGER, W. M. Plant Physiol. **32**, 136 (1957a).
HUMPHREYS, T. E., and DUGGER, W. M. Plant Physiol. **32**, 530 (1957b).
JAMES, W. O. *Plant Respiration*, Clarendon Press, Oxford (1953).
JAMES, W. O., JAMES, G. M., and BUNTING, A. H. Biochem. Jour. **35**, 588 (1941).
JAMES, W. O., and HORA, F. B. Ann. Botany (N.S.) **4**, 107 (1940).
JAMES, W. O., and RITCHIE, A. Proc. Roy. Soc. **B143**, 302 (1955).
KOSTYCHEV, S. *Plant Respiration* (C. J. LYON, ed.), Blakiston, Philadelphia (1927).
KROTKOV, G., COWIE, L., and REED, G. B. Plant Physiol. **30**, iv (1955).
LATIES, G. G. Arch. Biochem. Biophys. **20**, 284 (1949).
MILLER, G. W. Plant Physiol. **33**, 199 (1958).
MILLER, G. W., and EVANS, H. J. Plant Physiol. **32**, 346 (1957).
MILLERD, A., BONNER, J., AXELROD, B., and BANDURSKI, R. S. Proc. Nat. Acad. Sci. **37**, 855 (1951).
NEAL, G. E., and BEEVERS, H. Biochem. Jour. **74**, 409 (1960).
NEISH, A. C. Can. J. Biochem. Physiol. **33**, 658 (1955).
NEUBERG, C., and GOTTSCHALK, A. Biochem. Zeitschr. **160**, 256 (1925).
NEWCOMB, E. H. Am. Jour. Botany **37**, 264 (1950).
PHILLIPS, J. W. Am. Jour. Botany **34**, 62 (1947).
RACKER, E. Adv. in Enzymology **15**, 141 (1954).
RACKER, E. Physiol. Rev. **35**, 1 (1955).
RAMSHORN, K. Flora **145**, 1 (1957a).
RAMSHORN, K. Flora **146**, 178 (1957b).
RUHLAND, W., and RAMSHORN, K. Planta **28**, 471 (1938).
SALTMAN, P. D. Jour. Biol. Chem. **200**, 145 (1953).
SHAW, M., and SAMBORSKI, D. J. Can. J. Botany **35**, 389 (1957).
SHAW, M., SAMBORSKI, D. H., and OAKS, A. Can. J. Botany **36**, 233 (1958).
SUMNER, J. B., and MYRBACK, K. *The Enzymes*, Academic Press, New York (1951).
STUMPF, P. K. Jour. Biol. Chem. **176**, 233 (1948).
STUMPF, P. K. Jour. Biol. Chem. **182**, 261 (1950).
STUMPF, P. K. Ann. Rev. Plant Physiol. **3**, 17 (1952).
STUMPF, P. K. Plant Physiol. **30**, 55 (1955).
TANG, P. S., TAI, Y. L., and LEE, C. K. Scientia Sinica **5**, 509 (1956).
TEWFIK, S., and STUMPF, P. K. Am. Jour. Botany **36**, 567 (1949).
TEWFIK, S., and STUMPF, P. K. Jour. Biol. Chem. **192**, 519 (1951).
THOMAS, M., RANSON, S. L., and RICHARDSON, A. *Plant Physiology* (4th ed.), Churchill, London (1956).
TOLBERT, N. E., and ZILL, L. P. Plant Physiol. **29**, 288 (1954).
WARBURG, O., CHRISTIAN, W., and GRIESE, A. Biochem. Zeitschr. **282**, 157 (1935).

Chapter 3

The TCA Cycle:

The Utilization of Pyruvate

The most important outcome of the sequences outlined in the previous chapters is the generation of pyruvate. To be sure, significant quantities of pyridine nucleotides are reduced (the amounts depending on how much glucose is channeled through the pentose phosphate pathway), and some ATP is produced, but these are small in comparison with the amounts and utility of the products which arise in the subsequent utilization of pyruvate.

We can deduce that pyruvate must be actively oxidized in plant cells because it is found only in small amounts and the characteristic product of its "anaerobic" utilization—ethanol—does not normally accumulate in air. The details of its oxidation in plants have become clear in the past ten to fifteen years, and the investigations have followed closely the pattern established in pioneer work with animal tissues. In the outcome, several of the acids which were well known as components of plant tissues, e.g., malate, fumarate, and citrate, were implicated in the oxidative breakdown of pyruvate. Speculation about the organic acids, which are present in relatively large amounts in plants, had centered largely on their roles as end products of glucose breakdown or as intermediates in protein metabolism. With the elucidation of the tricarboxylic acid (TCA) cycle by Krebs and others in the 1930's, it seemed clear that a considerable amount of information about acid metabolism in plants could be neatly accounted for (Chibnall, 1939). Subsequent work has justified the view that the TCA cycle is the major route of pyruvate utilization in plant, as in animal, cells; for most of the observations on the details of its function in mammalian tissues as a major source of reduced nucleotides and of precursors for a variety of synthetic events there are now parallel observations from work with plant materials. In this chapter we will be concerned with the evidence that the TCA cycle exists as a potentially functional unit in plants and with the experiments on intact tissues which show that it does so function in the respiratory breakdown of pyruvate.

The recognition that the enzymes of the TCA cycle were housed in the functional units, the mitochondria, in animal cells was a most important finding in the elucidation of the reactions shown in Figure 5. Several of the enzymes catalyzing individual reactions had been detected in aqueous extracts from plants before 1950 (see James, 1953), and succinic dehydrogenase was known to occur on particles associated with the cytochrome system (Bhagvat and Hill, 1951). It is now clear that in plants also, although soluble counterparts of some of the "particulate" enzymes exist, the isolated mitochondria are themselves capable of carrying out all the reactions of the TCA cycle.

It was in the early fifties that the first successful isolation of mitochondrial particles was achieved (Millerd et al., 1951; Laties, 1953a,b; Davies, 1953). In the intervening years, many plant parts have yielded active mitochondria to many investigators (see Hackett, 1953, 1959, for summaries). The tissues examined include leaves, flowers, fleshy fruits, various parts of seedlings, underground storage organs, and tobacco callus. Not all of these have been thoroughly examined for their ability to carry out all of the reactions of the TCA cycle. Frequently the oxidation of two or three substrates only has been demonstrated. Nevertheless, it now seems certain that successful isolation of oxidative particles can be achieved from most higher plant tissues when due regard is paid to their known fragility and susceptibilities (Chapter 6).

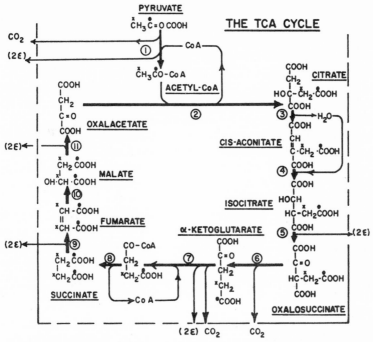

FIGURE 5.—Reactions of the tricarboxylic acid cycle. The fate of the pyruvate carbons during the first traverse of the cycle is indicated. The enzymes catalyzing the numbered reactions are 1, pyruvic oxidase complex; 2, condensing enzyme; 3, 4, aconitase; 5, 6, isocitric dehydrogenase; 7, α-ketoglutaric oxidase complex; 8, phosphorylating enzyme; 9, succinic dehydrogenase; 10, fumarase; 11, malic dehydrogenase. The pairs of electrons (2ϵ) removed by the dehydrogenases are transferred by accessory enzymes to O_2.

Clearly the important attribute of particles containing all of the enzymes of the TCA cycle (with the associated electron-transfer and oxidase systems) is the ability to induce the sustained oxidation of pyruvate when a catalytic amount of any member acid is provided. It should be noted that a necessary but insufficient criterion for the operation of the cycle in particles is the ability to oxidize individual acids. For when such an acid is added in substrate amounts, its oxidation may proceed for only one or two stages, due apparently to the preempting of the electron-transfer sequence by electrons arising from these stages (see below). And, in any event, the oxidation would proceed no further than oxalacetic acid unless this was subsequently converted to pyruvic acid and thence to acetyl-CoA (Figure 5). Even so, individual acids are frequently found to be oxidized at unexpectedly different rates. A feature of mitochondria from several plants which might explain such discrepancies is their response to added cofactors such as DPN, CoA, and TPP (Beevers and Walker, 1956; Lieberman and Biale, 1956). Only in the presence of all of these components were high rates of oxidation of all of the individual members of the TCA cycle achieved in mitochondria from castor-bean endosperm (Table VI).

Freebairn and Remmert (1957) have pointed out that only infrequently has the complete oxidation to CO_2 and H_2O of individual acids been demonstrated. They provided data showing that this was in fact achieved for oxidation by mitochondria from cabbage, which was one of the better sources

TABLE VI

EFFECTS OF COFACTORS ON OXIDATION OF TCA-CYCLE ACIDS* BY CASTOR-BEAN MITOCHONDRIA (BEEVERS AND WALKER, 1956)

Cofactors Added	Malate	Fumarate	Succinate	Citrate	Cis-aconitate	Isocitrate	α-Keto-glutarate	Oxalacetate + Pyruvate†
None	14	22	128	64	68	60	40	0
ATP 1 mg	44	26	264	104	84	66	102	—
DPN 1 mg	32	18	98	125	92	100	148	—
ATP + DPN	84	66	448	270	202	180	256	—
ATP + DPN + CoA (0.1 mg)	376	370	600	376	294	290	304	0
ATP + DPN + CoA + TPP (0.5 mg)	—	—	—	—	—	—	386	396

* Substrate concentration 0.01 M except for isocitrate, which was 0.02 M DL-isocitrate.

† Oxalacetate 0.001 M + pyruvate 0.01 M. The values shown are in μl. O_2 uptake/hr.

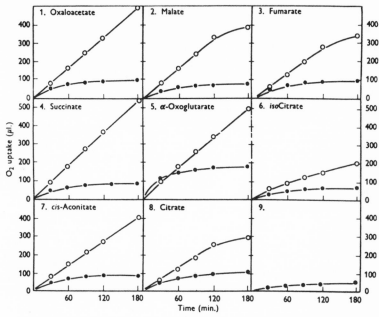

FIGURE 6.—The effectiveness of acids of the TCA cycle as sparkers of pyruvate oxidation by mitochondria from castor bean. The lower curve (solid circles) in each case represents the O_2 uptake observed on adding 2 micromoles of the named acid to the mitochondria fortified with cofactors. The upper curve (open circles) represents the O_2 uptake observed when 20 micromoles of pyruvate were added in addition. Graph 9 shows the O_2 uptake observed in the presence or absence of pyruvate when no second acid was included. (Walker and Beevers, 1956.)

of active mitochondria out of some forty tissues examined (see also Smillie, 1955, and Beaudreau and Remmert, 1955).

Figure 6 shows a commonly observed result. By themselves the mitochondria are not capable of oxidizing pyruvate. However, when a catalytic amount of any member of the TCA cycle is added, a rapid rate of oxidation is induced. It should be emphasized that the amount of O_2 absorbed by far exceeds that which would have been required for the complete oxidation of the sparker acids; there is no doubt that pyruvate was being oxidized. The fact that carbon from pyruvate was actually traversing the cycle as required from Figure 6 was

TABLE VII

THE ACCUMULATION OF C^{14} IN CO_2 AND ACIDS OF THE TRICARBOXYLIC ACID
CYCLE FROM PYRUVATE-2-C^{14} SUPPLIED TO PREPARATIONS OF LUPINE
MITOCHONDRIA (BRUMMOND AND BURRIS, 1953)

Trapping Acid Added	Per Cent C^{14} Found in Trapping Acid Recovered	Per Cent C^{14} Found in CO_2 Formed	Per Cent C^{14} Found in Citrate Formed	Per Cent C^{14} Found in Malate Recovered
Citrate	6.5	1.0	—	0.7
Cis-aconitate	1.5	0.5	30.2	0.6
Isocitrate	2.2	1.0	49.0	5.0
Oxalosuccinate	0.5	1.5	—	—
α-Ketoglutarate	7.5	1.0	—	—
Succinate	5.5	1.0	—	—
Fumarate	4.4	1.5	—	—
Malate	2.0	1.0	10.9	—
Oxalacetate	2.3	1.5	—	—
Pyruvate alone	—	0.2	—	—

firmly established by Brummond and Burris (1953). As shown in Table VII, these authors provided pyruvate-2-C^{14} and malate as the sparker acid to lupine mitochondria, and by adding also trapping amounts of the individual acids in different experiments they were able to show that C^{14} was incorporated into each of these during pyruvate oxidation (see also Freebairn and Remmert, 1957). A further important finding was that the citrate produced when only malate and pyruvate-2-C^{14} were added had the same specific activity (c.p.m./micromole) as the original pyruvate. In other work with labeled substrates it has been established that the order of appearance of the carbons of the entering C-2 unit as CO_2 is that predicted from Figure 5 (Stanley, 1957).

Further evidence for the operation of the sequence as outlined has come from experiments in which the accumulation of intermediates has been induced either by adding an excess of a particular substrate or by selectively inhibiting particular stages. Thus, for example, citrate accumulation has been demonstrated when pyruvate and malate (as sparker) were provided to a variety of mitochondria (Davies, 1953; Avron and Biale, 1957a,b). Again, when succinate oxidation was interfered with by malonate, succinate accumulated from

TABLE VIII

Oxidation of TCA-Cycle Acids and the Effects of Malonate and
Arsenite. Avocado Mitochondria with Cofactor Supplement (Avron
and Biale, 1957)

SUBSTRATE	% Inhibition of O_2 Uptake	
	0.01 M Malonate	0.001 M Arsenite
Citrate	42	55
Cis-aconitate	25	52
α-Ketoglutarate	48	100
Succinate	76	25
Fumarate	34	81
Malate	21	84
Pyruvate + malate sparker	74	94

citrate or α-ketoglutarate; and arsenite, which prevents keto
acid oxidation, induced the accumulation of α-ketoglutarate
when citrate was the substrate (Table VIII). Davies (1954),
working with mitochondria from peas, was able to show the
operation of several of the individual steps of the cycle, and
Price and Thimann (1954) have studied the malic, succinic,
and α-ketoglutaric dehydrogenases from similar material.

Although little direct work has been done on the enzymes
concerned with the early steps of pyruvate oxidation, there is
no reason to doubt that these are the same as those elucidated
from other tissues, in which lipoic acid, TPP, DPN, and CoA
are all part of the enzyme complex by which pyruvate is converted to acetyl-CoA (Table IX).

TABLE IX

Outline of Reactions in Keto Acid Oxidation*

Pyruvate + TPP → TPP addition compound + CO_2
TPP addition compound + Lipoic acid (S-S) → TPP + Acetyl-lipoic acid
Acetyl-lipoic acid + CoA → Acetyl-CoA + Lipoic acid (SH)
Lipoic acid (SH) + DPN → Lipoic acid (S-S) + DPNH

Sum: Pyruvate + CoA + DPN → Acetyl-CoA + CO_2 + DPNH

* The reactions shown occur in the pyruvate oxidase complex. α-Ketoglutarate is oxidized to CO_2 and succinyl-CoA by an analogous sequence.

Some of the evidence in favor of this view is as follows:

a. Citrate formation from pyruvate and oxalacetate was shown to require CoA, and when acetate was supplied instead of pyruvate, its conversion to acetyl-CoA was a prerequisite to its incorporation into citrate (Funahashi and Akazawa, 1954).

b. Specific requirements for DPN, CoA, and TPP have been shown for pyruvate oxidation by some mitochondria (Walker and Beevers, 1956).

c. Pyruvate oxidation was induced if, instead of the usual sparker, a bacterial transacetylase which consumes acetyl-CoA by converting it to acetyl phosphate was provided (Walker and Beevers, 1956).

The participation of acetyl-CoA can also be inferred from experiments in which acetate oxidation has been induced by mitochondria fortified with cofactors (Stumpf and Barber, 1956) and from the fact that sulfanilamide may be acetylated *in vivo* (Jones and Wignall, 1955). An acetate-activating system has been detected in a variety of tissues (e.g., Millerd and Bonner, 1954; Patrick, 1957).

Thus, although the individual enzymes have not been intensively studied, there is now ample and direct evidence for stating that mitochondria from plants carry out the reactions as shown in Figure 5. Their activities are not of course limited to these reactions. The action of accessory enzymes in the mitochondria results in the diversion of TCA intermediates in synthetic events, particularly those leading to proteins through the amino acids. For example, the synthesis of glutamate and, by transamination, aspartate has been demonstrated in mitochondrial preparations. In addition, the TCA cycle is a source of succinyl-CoA (Kaufman and Alivisatos, 1955), an important precursor of other cellular constituents (Figure 24).

It seems likely that the levels of the TCA-cycle intermediates in the mitochondria when they are oxidizing pyruvate *in vivo* are uniformly low, and thus, if intermediates are drained off, there will be immediate effects on the regeneration of the C-2 acceptor, oxalacetate. Reactions whereby replenishment of oxalacetate, or of 4-carbon acids related to it, thus become of vital importance for the continued operation of the TCA cycle. There are at least three ways in which such a replenishment may occur by CO_2 fixation:

a. Production of oxalacetate by the phospho-enol pyruvate (PEP) carboxylase reaction,

Phospho-enol pyruvate $+ CO_2 \rightarrow$ Oxalacetate $+$ iP.

b. Production of oxalacetate by the PEP carboxykinase,

Phospho-enol pyruvate $+ ADP + CO_2 \rightleftarrows$
Oxalacetate $+ ATP.$

c. Malate production by malic enzyme,

Pyruvate $+ CO_2 + TPNH \rightleftarrows$ Malate $+ TPN.$

It has been shown that when they are provided with PEP and CO_2 some mitochondria do not require the addition of a "sparker" acid, and this is no doubt due to the generation of the oxalacetate acceptor by reactions a and b, above. The enzymes have been shown to be present in plant mitochondria (Davies, 1953; Mazelis and Vennesland, 1957; Young and Graham, 1958; Benedict, 1960; and Walker, 1957).

A further possible mechanism of replenishment is afforded by the glyoxylate cycle (p. 213), but the limited distribution of the requisite enzymes makes it unlikely that it is of general utility except in the specialized tissue of fatty seedlings.

We may now examine the evidence that pyruvate oxidation via the TCA cycle is an important component of the respiration of living plant cells.

Occurrence and gross interconversion of the TCA-cycle acids. It is of interest first of all that in all of those tissues which have been carefully examined, evidence for the presence of the acids of the cycle has been found. Further, it has been established that large-scale interconversion such as the formation of citrate from malate, and of malate and citrate from succinate and fumarate, becomes understandable when the reactions of the TCA cycle are considered (Vickery and colleagues; see Burris, 1953, for a summary).

Effects of acids of the TCA cycle on respiration. There is now ample evidence that internal factors other than the supply of intermediates usually regulate respiratory rates in plant cells (Chapter 7). In some tissues, however, stimulations of O_2 uptake have been observed following addition of acids such as malate and citrate, and this has been taken as evidence for the operation of the TCA cycle. Such a deduction is not permissible because the acid may itself be partially oxidized (perhaps even by extramitochondrial enzymes) and bring about increases in O_2 uptake without necessarily giving rise to oxalacetate and thus inducing a greater rate of pyruvate oxidation in the TCA cycle.

Experiments with C^{14}-labeled acids. There is now a large amount of information from experiments in which relatively small amounts of labeled acids or other substrates have been provided to plant tissues and the appearance of C^{14} noted in other members of the cycle. Burris and his colleagues carried out pioneering investigations along these lines, and the rapid incorporation of C^{14} from malate, formate, and glycolate was described (see Burris, 1953). These authors suggested that their data could be accommodated by a functioning TCA cycle with ancillary reactions, but they were led to doubt that it functioned rapidly enough in some tissues because of the unequal specific activity of the various acids even after long exposure to the C^{14}-labeled precursors. It is recognized, however, that since a large fraction of any particular acid in the cell may be present in pools (e.g., the vacuole) in which turnover is slow, those acids at the metabolic centers (e.g., the mitochondria) might well have reached equal specific activity quite early in the experiments.

Strong evidence for the operation of the TCA cycle comes from experiments in which plant tissues have been provided with specifically labeled pyruvates. Buhler *et al.* (1956) demonstrated that pyruvate-2-C^{14} was utilized in tomato fruit, and malate (with most of its C^{14} in the carboxyl groups) and citrate were among the products. Neal and Beevers (1960) have compared the utilization of pyruvate-1-, 2-, and 3-C^{14} in a variety of plant tissues. The first point of interest is the order

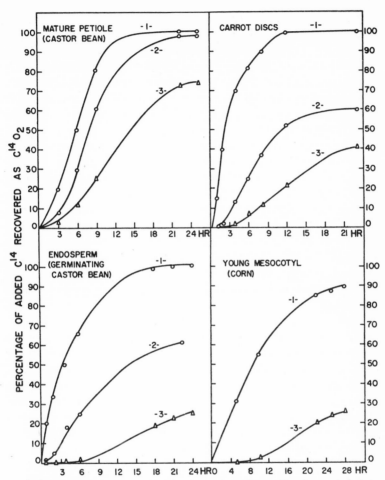

FIGURE 7.—Pyruvate-C[14] utilization by various tissues. Equal samples of the named tissues were incubated with equal amounts of pyruvate-1-, 2-, or 3-C[14], and the respired CO_2 was assayed for C[14]. (Neal and Beevers, 1960; ap Rees and Beevers, 1960.)

in which the individual carbons make their appearance in the respired CO_2 (Figure 7). In the several tissues examined, C-1 of pyruvate begins to appear in the CO_2 at once and continues to be given off at a high rate until it is quantitatively recovered. It is followed in turn by C-2 and C-3, whose appearance as CO_2 occurs in some tissues only after quite noticeable lag periods.

It will be realized from Figure 5 that C-2 of the original pyruvate would not begin to appear as CO_2 until after the isocitric dehydrogenase step in the second turn of the cycle and that a further complete turn would be required before any C-3 appeared as CO_2. The changing contributions of the various carbons with time, shown in Figure 7, are thus clearly consistent with the occurrence of an initial oxidative decarboxylation to acetyl-CoA, followed by introduction into the TCA cycle.

Carbon from the cycling acetyl unit, as it passes into the various TCA-cycle intermediates, is subject to withdrawal in events such as amino acid synthesis and transfer to inert pools. And since its sojourn in the cycle is more prolonged, C-3 of the original pyruvate is more likely to suffer this fate than is C-2. These predictions are fulfilled in the behavior of C-2 and C-3 shown in Figure 7. Not only are the maximum rates of appearance of these carbons successively lower than those for C-1, but even after prolonged periods they are far from completely recovered as CO_2, and the retention of C-3 is considerably greater than that of C-2. Tissue analyses have revealed that the major fate of C_2 and C_3 in growing tissue was protein and amino acid. In *Bryophyllum* leaves these carbons were found in the large organic acid pools. It is of great interest that the release of C_2 and C_3 as CO_2 approached 100% only in the fully mature tissue of the petiole (see p. 195). Of further significance to the question of the operation of the cycle is the finding that C_2 and C_3 were found almost immediately in the organic acid fraction, and before these carbons were contributing to the CO_2. The time curves from the growing tissue gave clear evidence of a rapid movement of the two-carbon units into acids of the TCA cycle and a subsequent progressive incorporation into the amino acid and protein components. C-1 did not contribute significantly to the organic acid or nitrogen fractions.

Free acetate is not normally thought of as a major plant

metabolite, although reports of its occurrence are now quite frequent. Nevertheless, when it is provided in small amounts, several plant tissues have been shown to be capable of metabolizing it—presumably after conversion to acetyl-CoA. It has been shown that conversion to CO_2 is a major fate, with C-1 contributing in larger measure. The prompt appearance of acetate carbon in intermediates of the TCA cycle and related amino acids (Zbinowsky and Burris, 1952; Canvin and Beevers, 1960) is clear evidence of its utilization by this pathway. Wang, Hansen, and Christensen (1953) presented valuable data from tomato fruit supplied with acetate-C^{14}. When the C^{14} distributions in the citrate and malate were compared, it seemed highly probable that the acetate unit was traversing the cycle in the predicted manner. In longer-term experiments with wheat leaves, Bilinski and McConnell (1957a,b) showed that C^{14} from labeled acetate was incorporated into a variety of amino acids in the protein. Their results on the distribution of C^{14} from specifically labeled acetate in aspartic and glutamic acids of the wheat gluten harmonized very well with the concept that they had been produced by diversion of the corresponding TCA-cycle intermediates.

Thus, although acetate units might be diverted along other synthetic pathways (fat, cyclic, and isoprenoid compounds), the foregoing evidence points unmistakably to the TCA cycle as a major pathway of its utilization. Since this is so, carbons 1 and 2 of acetate would be expected to behave in the same way as carbons 2 and 3 of pyruvate, respectively. Such is indeed the case in the experiments discussed above. In addition, Bilinski and McConnell (1958a) have emphasized this similarity as a major feature of their work with wheat plants. In the metabolism of castor-bean endosperm the correspondence is clear (Canvin and Beevers, 1960; Neal and Beevers, 1960).

Experiments with inhibitors. The use of malonate, a classical inhibitor of succinic dehydrogenase, seems to offer an especially useful tool in deciding whether the TCA sequence operates in the respiration of a particular tissue. However, the early work with this inhibitor on plant tissues led to contradictory conclusions. Some of the anomalies can be reasonably ascribed to difficulties of penetration of the inhibitor when it is applied at relatively high pH levels, a problem common to all weak acids (Simon and Beevers, 1952). Further difficulties in the way of interpretation are posed by observations on the inhibition of other reactions by malonate at the high levels usually employed (see discussion in Vickery and Palmer, 1957). Nevertheless, it is now clear that sizable inhibitions of O_2 uptake, which can reasonably be ascribed to interference with succinic dehydrogenase, can be achieved, and in a variety of tissues. Furthermore, in some of these, the anticipated pile-up of succinate has been demonstrated to occur (Bonner, 1948; Laties, 1947, 1949a,b; Vickery and Palmer, 1957), and, in addition, succinate formation from fumarate under malonate treatment has been observed (Bonner, 1948; Laties, 1949a). Recent work emphasizes that, as its CoA derivative, malonate may have important metabolic roles in fat metabolism (Chapter 12). We may also note that quite appreciable levels of malonate are found in some plant tissues, particularly legumes (Bentley, 1952; Soldatenkov and Mazurova, 1957; Young and Shannon, 1958), and it is apparently metabolized by a variety of plant tissues (Shannon et al., 1959).

Arsenite, which interferes with keto acid oxidation in mitochondria (Lieberman and Biale, 1956; Avron and Biale, 1957a), induces quite striking inhibitions of O_2 uptake of intact tissues (Beevers and Gibbs, 1954; ap Rees and Beevers, 1960).

Fluoroacetate, which is apparently similar enough to acetate to substitute for it in the activating and condensing enzyme systems, is another inhibitor of the TCA cycle. In animal tissues the fluorocitrate which is formed is apparently not an acceptable substrate for further reactions, and the cycle is said to be "jammed" at this stage (Peters, 1952). In some plant tissues also fluoroacetate is able to bring about inhibitions of O_2 uptake.

There is also evidence that α,α'-dipyridyl is an inhibitor of aconitase activity, and thus it is able to inhibit O_2 uptake of barley embryos and roots. Citrate, accumulation was induced (James, 1956).

Two further treatments which are found to have at least indirect effects on the TCA cycle are exposure to O_2 at high pressure and to high concentrations (greater than 50%) of CO_2. Barker and his colleagues (Barker and Mapson, 1955; Turner and Quartley, 1956; Quartley and Turner, 1957; Barker, Quartley, and Turner, 1959) have shown that in pure O_2 at 1–5 atmospheres the CO_2 output from a variety of tissues, including peas, apples, and potatoes, is progressively inhibited. At the same time distinctive changes were noted in the levels of various acids of the TCA cycle. Citrate and, later, pyruvate accumulated in the tissues, while the levels of malate and α-ketoglutarate and (in peas and apples) oxalacetate declined (see Figure 8). Ethanol accumulation was observed in

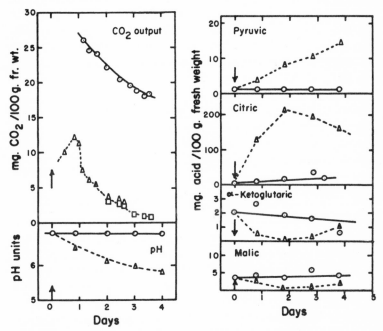

FIGURE 8.—O_2 block of the TCA cycle. Peas were transferred to 5 atm. O_2 at the time indicated by the arrow. Note the depression of CO_2 output and pH resulting from the treatment and the specific effects on individual acids (after Turner and Quartley, 1956).

apples, and lactate appeared in the potatoes. The authors point out that the most reasonable way of accounting for these results is that an "O_2 block" develops between the citrate and α-ketoglutarate, probably due to an effect on aconitase. As a whole these findings are clearly indicative of a functioning TCA cycle in the untreated tissues.

Adverse effects of high partial pressures of CO_2 have been known for many years (Thomas, 1925, 1930; Foster, 1940). The induction of fermentation (CO_2-zymasis) even though the O_2 tension was maintained at the air value is a result of particular interest here. The later observation (Ranson, 1953; Hulme, 1956; Ulrich and Landry, 1956) that succinate accumulation was induced by CO_2 pointed to the succinoxidase system as a possible locus of action, and experiments with mitochondria (Ranson et al., 1957) have confirmed this suggestion.

The inhibition of O_2 uptake induced by the various reagents mentioned above are in keeping with what is known about their effects on enzymes of the TCA cycle. A second point, and one which is important in establishing that the cycle is the major route of pyruvate oxidation, is the concomitant effects on CO_2 output. Clearly, if the TCA cycle is slowed down by a specific inhibitor, the regeneration of oxalacetate will be diminished and the oxidation of pyruvate will then not be able to keep pace with its production. Under these conditions, even though O_2 is present and the oxidase systems are active, a diversion to ethanol and CO_2 might be predicted, and it does indeed occur (Table X).

Thus, increases in R.Q. have been observed when fluoroacetate, malonate, and arsenite were provided at appropriate levels. The induction of aerobic fermentation may be inferred from these values, since ethanol accumulation has been shown to occur in the presence of malonate (Beevers, 1952) and arsenite (Beevers and Gibbs, 1954). High CO_2 levels (Thomas, 1925) and O_2 levels (Turner and Quartley, 1956; Barker et al., 1959) also induce the accumulation of ethanol. A feature of the fermentation induced by these inhibitors of the TCA cycle (which distinguishes it from fermentation

TABLE X

EXPERIMENTAL INDUCTION OF AEROBIC FERMENTATION*

Reagent	Locus of Action	Acetaldehyde Accumulation
HCN	Terminal oxidase	Low
CO	Terminal oxidase	Low
H_2S	Terminal oxidase	Low
Malonate	Succinic dehydrogenase	High
Arsenite	α-Keto acid oxidation	High
Fluoroacetate	Jamming at citrate	—
CO_2 (>50%)	Succinic oxidase	High
O_2 (>1 atm.)	Citrate breakdown	—
DNP	ATP production in oxidative phosphorylation (indirect glycolytic stimulant)	High

* All of the treatments resulted in a noticeably increased R.Q. or alcohol production or both when these were investigated. The "high" entries in the acetaldehyde column indicate that more acetaldehyde was produced in relation to alcohol in these experiments than was found anaerobically or in the presence of inhibitors of the terminal oxidase (see text).

induced by stopping terminal oxidase activity) is the appearance of acetaldehyde in measurable amounts. The incomplete reduction of acetaldehyde may be ascribed to the fact that under these conditions the aerobic mechanism for DPNH oxidation remains unimpaired.

The central role of pyruvate and the TCA cycle in aerobic respiration is further emphasized by treatments which are known to have their immediate effects on reactions outside the cycle itself. Thus, depriving the tissues of O_2 leads to a stoppage of electron transfer and hence of pyruvate oxidation. Diversion to ethanol and CO_2 is the usual result. It is of interest that changes in the levels of some of the TCA-cycle intermediates have been shown to occur on transfer to N_2 (Ranson, 1953; Hulme, 1954; Barber, 1957; Krupka and Towers, 1958). Similarly, by inhibiting the oxidase systems with cyanide, azide, CO, or H_2S, pyruvate oxidation is prevented, and it is shunted to fermentation products (Table X).

Most tissues apparently contain pyruvic decarboxylase, but

in spite of this the aerobic oxidation system normally filches all of the pyruvate. Some recent work showing that the K_m of the yeast pyruvate oxidation system for the substrate is about one-tenth that of the decarboxylase (Holzer and Goedde, 1957) may well account for this finding. The foregoing experiments indicate that this prevailing balance can be overcome by incapacitating the oxidation system in one of several ways. It is of interest also that diversion to ethanol and CO_2 occurs when the capacity of the oxidation system is saturated. This can be achieved most easily by supplying an excess of pyruvate from without or, more subtly, by inducing the cells to produce more of their own pyruvate than they can cope with oxidatively. DNP, which indirectly brings about a stimulation in the rate of glycolysis (p. 153), produces such an effect (Newcomb, 1950; Beevers, 1953). It was deduced from the effects of DNP on O_2 uptake and CO_2 output and ethanol production that tissues differ in their ability to deal with extra supplies of pyruvate; in some, e.g., corn root and coleoptiles and sunflower epicotyl, slight increases result in a "spilling over" into acetaldehyde and ethanol, while in others, e.g., carrot slices, the oxidation system can still cope successfully with a two- to threefold stimulation in the rate of pyruvate production (Beevers, 1953).

REFERENCES

AP REES, T., and BEEVERS, H. Plant Physiol. 35, 839 (1960).
AVRON, M., and BIALE, J. B. Plant Physiol. 32, 100 (1957a).
AVRON, M., and BIALE, J. B. Jour. Biol. Chem. 225, 699 (1957b).
BARBER, D. A. Nature 180, 1053 (1957).
BARKER, J., and MAPSON, L. W. Proc. Roy. Soc. Lond. B143, 523 (1955).
BARKER, J., QUARTLEY, C. E., and TURNER, E. R. Proc. Roy. Soc. Lond. B152, 88 (1960).
BEAUDREAU, G. S., and REMMERT, L. F. Arch. Biochem. Biophys. 55, 469 (1955).
BEEVERS, H. Plant Physiol. 27, 725 (1952).
BEEVERS, H. Am. Jour. Botany 40, 91 (1953).
BEEVERS, H., and GIBBS, M. Plant Physiol. 29, 318 (1954).
BEEVERS, H., and WALKER, D. A. Biochem Jour. 62, 114 (1956).
BENEDICT, C. R. Ph.D. Thesis, Purdue University, Lafayette, Indiana (1960).
BENTLEY, L. E. Nature 170, 847 (1952).
BHAGVAT, K., and HILL, R. New Phytol. 50, 112 (1951).
BILINSKI, E., and MCCONNELL, W. B. Can. J. Biochem. Physiol. 35, 357 (1957a).
BILINSKI, E., and MCCONNELL, W. B. Can. J. Biochem. Physiol. 35, 365 (1957b).
BILINSKI, E., and MCCONNELL, W. B. Can. J. Biochem. Physiol. 36, 381 (1958).

BONNER, J. Arch. Biochem. **17**, 311 (1948).
BONNER, J. Am. Jour. Botany **36**, 429 (1949).
BARRON, E. S. G., LINK, G. K. K., KLEIN, R. M., and MICHEL, B. E. Arch. Biochem. Biophys. **28**, 377 (1950).
BONNER, W. D., and THIMANN, K. V. Am. Jour. Botany **37**, 66 (1950).
BRUMMOND, D. O., and BURRIS, R. H. Proc. Nat. Acad. Sci. **39**, 754 (1953).
BUHLER, D. R., HANSEN, E., CHRISTENSEN, B. E., and WANG, C. H. Plant Physiol. **31**, 192 (1956).
BURRIS, R. H. Ann. Rev. Plant Physiol. **4**, 91 (1953).
CANVIN, D. T., and BEEVERS, H. Plant Physiol. **35**, xv (1960).
CHIBNALL, A. C. *Protein Metabolism in the Plant,* Yale University Press (1939).
DAVIES, D. D. Jour. Exp. Botany **4**, 173 (1953).
DAVIES, D. D. Proc. Roy. Soc. **B1952**, 155 (1954).
FREEBAIRN, H. T., and REMMERT, L. F. Physiol. Plant. **10**, 20 (1957).
FOSTER, W. E. Ph.D. Thesis, Durham, England (1940).
FUNAHASHI, S., and AKAZAWA, T. Jour. Agr. Chem. Soc. Japan **28**, 574 (1954).
HACKETT, D. P. Inter. Rev. Cytol. **4**, 143 (1953).
HACKETT, D. P. Ann. Rev. Plant Physiol. **10**, 113 (1959).
HOLZER, H., and GOEDDE, H. W. Biochem. Zeitschr. **329**, 175 (1957).
HULME, A. C. Proceedings 8th Int. Botanical Congress, p. 394 (1954).
HULME, A. C. Nature **178**, 218 (1956).
JAMES, W. O. *Plant Respiration,* Clarendon Press, Oxford (1953).
JAMES, W. O. New Phytol. **55**, 269 (1956).
JONES, R., and WIGNALL, J. Nature **175**, 207 (1955).
KAUFMAN, S., and ALIVISATOS, S. G. A. Jour. Biol. Chem. **216**, 141 (1955).
KRUPKA, R. M., and TOWERS, G. H. N. Can. J. Botany **36**, 165 (1958).
LIEBERMAN, M., and BIALE, J. B. Plant Physiol. **31**, 425 (1956).
LATIES, G. G. Am. Jour. Botany **34**, 601 (1947).
LATIES, G. G. Arch. Biochem. **22**, 8 (1949).
LATIES, G. G. Physiol. Plant. **6**, 199 (1953a).
LATIES, G. G. Physiol. Plant. **6**, 215 (1953b).
MAZELIS, M., and VENNESLAND, B. Plant Physiol. **32**, 591 (1957).
MILLERD, A., BONNER, J., AXELROD, B., and BANDURSKI, R. S. Proc. Nat. Acad. Sci. **37**, 855 (1951).
MILLERD, A., and BONNER, J. Arch. Biochem. Biophys. **49**, 343 (1954).
NEAL, G. E., and BEEVERS, H. Biochem. Jour. **74**, 409 (1960).
NEWCOMB, E. H. Am. Jour. Botany **37**, 264 (1950).
PATRICK, A. D. Nature **180**, 37 (1957).
PETERS, R. A. Proc. Roy. Soc. **B139**, 143 (1952).
PRICE, C. A., and THIMANN, K. V. Plant Physiol. **29**, 113 (1954).
PROKOSHEV, S. M., and ROMANOVA, A. K. Doklady Akad. Nauk. S.S.S.R. **110**, 613 (1956).
QUARTLEY, C. E., and TURNER, E. R. Jour. Exp. Botany **8**, 250 (1957).
RANSON, S. L., WALKER, D. A., and CLARKE, I. D. Biochem. Jour. **66**, 57P (1957).
RANSON, S. L. Nature **172**, 252 (1953).
SHANNON, L. M., YOUNG, R. H., and DUDLEY, C. Nature **183**, 683 (1959).
SIMON, E. W., and BEEVERS, H. New Phytol. **51**, 163 (1952).
SMILLIE, R. M. Australian Jour. Sci. **17**, 217 (1955).
SOLDATENKOV, S. V., and MAZUROVA, T. A. Biokhimiya **22**, 345 (1957).
STANLEY, R. G. Plant Physiol. **32**, 409 (1957).
STUMPF, P. K., and BARBER, G. A. Plant Physiol. **31**, 304 (1956).

THOMAS, M. Biochem. Jour. **19,** 927 (1925).
THOMAS, J. Adv. Sci., p. 402 (1930).
TURNER, E. R., and QUARTLEY, C. E. Jour. Exp. Botany **7,** 362 (1956).
ULRICH, R., and LANDRY, J. Compt. rend. **242,** 2757 (1956).
VICKERY, H. B., and PALMER, J. K. Jour. Biol. Chem. **225,** 629 (1957).
WALKER, D. A. Biochem. Jour. **67,** 73 (1957).
WALKER, D. A., and BEEVERS, H. Biochem. Jour. **62,** 120 (1956).
WANG, C. H., HANSEN, E., and CHRISTENSEN, B. E. Plant Physiol. **28,** 741 (1953).
YOUNG, L. C. T., and GRAHAM, J. S. D. Nature **181,** 1071 (1958).
YOUNG, R. H., and SHANNON, L. M. Plant Physiol. **33,** 35 (1958).
ZBINOWSKY, V., and BURRIS, R. H. Plant Physiol. **27,** 240 (1952).

Chapter 4

Electron-Transfer

and Oxidase Systems

As long as they are living, most cells absorb O_2 continuously. Investigations of plant respiration have included a great deal of work on this aspect of the process. As in other tissues, O_2 participates in respiration only as the final acceptor of electrons (Vartapetyan and Kursanov, 1955). The respiratory substrates and intermediates do not themselves react with O_2; rather, the electrons removed during their oxidation are transferred by way of a series of carriers to compounds which are capable, under the appropriate conditions, of yielding electrons to O_2 with the formation of H_2O or occasionally H_2O_2.

It should be clear that this important feature of respiration is obscured in the over-all equation for the respiration of glucose as it is usually written:

$$C_6H_{12}O_6 + 6O_2 \rightarrow 6CO_2 + 6H_2O$$

In order to emphasize that the only fate of O_2 is reduction to water, the equation should be expanded to read:

$$C_6H_{12}O_6 + 6O_2 + 6H_2O \rightarrow 6CO_2 + 12H_2O$$

The appropriate conditions would be afforded if a compound which had accepted electrons originally removed from the substrate was itself autoxidizable. The natural electron acceptors, with some important exceptions, do not react with O_2 at finite rates, and the final step in the transfer depends on the catalytic abilities of more or less specific enzymes. Such enzymes are called oxidases or terminal oxidases. Some authors (e.g., Bonner, 1957) consider that since the term "oxidase" connotes a reaction with atmospheric oxygen, the addition of "terminal" is redundant. Unfortunately, the term "oxidase" is not always restricted to reactions in which electrons are transferred directly from the named substrate to O_2—e.g., "DPNH oxidase" and "succinic oxidase." In view of this, it is reasonable to continue to use the more specific "terminal oxidase" for the enzyme within such a complex which is responsible for the final reaction in which O_2 is reduced.

Work on oxidases from plants has had an interesting history. Enzymes which were capable of oxidizing substrates by means of atmospheric O_2 were found in a variety of plant saps in the 1920's and 1930's. The oxidation of phenols had indeed been demonstrated in plants before the turn of the century (Bertrand, 1895). The discovery of ascorbic acid oxidase further focused attention on the oxidizing abilities of clear extracts, and the catalytic abilities of these systems were so striking that it seemed almost inevitable that they would be important in plant respiration. In addition, the widespread occurrence in plants of other soluble enzymes, the peroxidases, and more recently of glycolic acid oxidase has attracted attention.

Evidence in favor of the participation of such enzymes was being gathered during the period when the role of the particulate cytochromes was being firmly established in animal and yeast cells, which do not contain a superfluity of active soluble oxidases. From the early work of Keilin (1925) it had been clear that plant cells, too, contain cytochromes; and starting with the work of Okunuki (1939) and Bhagvat and Hill (1951), increasing importance has been attached to these agents in the respiration of plants. Although a great deal has been done in the past fifteen years to reconstruct oxidation systems with soluble oxidases as the terminal link with O_2, this period has seen a swing to the view that, despite the undoubted potentialities of these enzymes, the cytochrome oxidase system, whose activity is so much less striking, is nevertheless the most important link from respiratory inter-mediates to atmospheric O_2.

In the following sections the various terminal oxidases will be discussed. The possible relevance of each to respiratory O_2 uptake depends on the ability of H-donating systems pro-duced in the reactions described earlier to reduce the product of the terminal oxidase action and so to set up a sustained O_2 uptake, with the respiratory intermediate being oxidized and the substrate for the terminal oxidase acting catalytically (Figure 9).

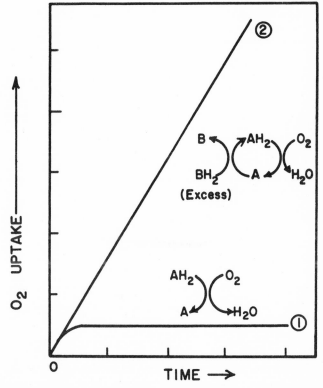

FIGURE 9.—Schematic representation of the O_2 uptake resulting when (1) a catalytic amount of substrate (AH_2) is added to a terminal oxidase and (2) an excess of some reducing system (BH_2) is also added.

PHENOL OXIDASES

When plant cells are disrupted by bruising or other means and exposed to the air, a frequent response is that brown pigments develop. If phenolic compounds such as catechol are added, this reaction is intensified. The browning can be ascribed to the oxidation of native phenols to quinones, which then react spontaneously with other cell constituents to give a variety of colored condensation products. Although other enzymes may contribute to the initial oxidation, the most important agents are copper-containing enzymes of the generic group phenol oxidases.

The rapid oxidation of native phenols upon injury suggests either that the enzymes and substrates are not in intimate contact in the intact cell or that the oxidation product is kept in the reduced form by H-donating systems. The possibility that the lack of pigment development in uninjured cells is due to poor accessibility of oxygen has no experimental support. The phenol oxidases can easily be obtained in solution and their activity demonstrated manometrically. Potato extracts are a particularly good source of enzyme, and a phenol oxidase has been highly purified from this material (Kubowitz, 1937). Exhaustive reviews on the action of phenol oxidases *in vitro* have been provided by Dawson and Tarpley (1951) and by Mason (1955), and these should be consulted for detailed information.

We can include in the general category of phenol oxidases the following activities: laccase, monophenol oxidase (tyrosinase), and polyphenol (catechol) oxidase. Extracts from individual plants may show different substrate specificities, and this is one of the bases for ascribing activity to laccase (p-phenylenediamine oxidized more rapidly than catechol) or tyrosinase (p-cresol or tyrosine more readily oxidized than diphenols). Laccase has been highly purified from *Rhus succidanea*; the best preparations contained about 0.25% of copper, a similar level to that found in potato phenol oxidase. An incompletely resolved question is that of the relationship of monophenolase to polyphenolase activity; it seems likely that these may be different aspects of the same enzyme (Mason, 1955).

Classification on the basis of substrate specificity is not completely satisfactory since not all of the possible natural substrates, which include anthocyanins, flavones, and aromatic acids, have been carefully studied. A great deal of work has been done with catechol as the su⁻. ⸴rate, although other polyphenols such as protocatechic acid, gallic acid, chlorogenic acid, and caffeic acid are usually present in larger amounts and are regarded as the "natural" substrates. Siegelman (1955) concluded that l-epicatechin filled this role in apple and pear skin. The oxidation rate with catechol as substrate is usually much higher than that with other phenols, but Roberts and Wood (1951) have shown that tea oxidase has a higher affinity for various natural catechins than for catechol. More recently Sisler and Evans (1958) have described a tobacco preparation which oxidized chlorogenic acid more efficiently than catechol, and Clayton (1959) has purified a similar enzyme which was not able to oxidize catechol; catechol in fact inhibited the oxidation of chlorogenic acid. These authors recognized that more than one enzyme capable of inducing oxidation of phenols was present, and Mason (1955) has emphasized the existing diversity in this group of enzymes.

The phenol oxidases have received serious consideration as terminal oxidases because the quinones produced during their oxidation can accept electrons from a variety of substances. For example, ascorbic acid, which is not a substrate for the enzyme, is rapidly oxidized by the quinone, and the sustained oxidation of ascorbate can be induced by the enzyme in the presence of a catalytic quantity of catechol (Figures 9 and 10).

In the presence of reducing agents the oxidation of phenol does not proceed beyond the quinonic (colorless) state (Figure 10), but in their absence secondary oxidations occur which lead to colored polymers. The quinone can be stabilized by reaction with primary or secondary amines (James et al., 1958; Hess, 1958; Beevers and James, 1948; Suzuki,

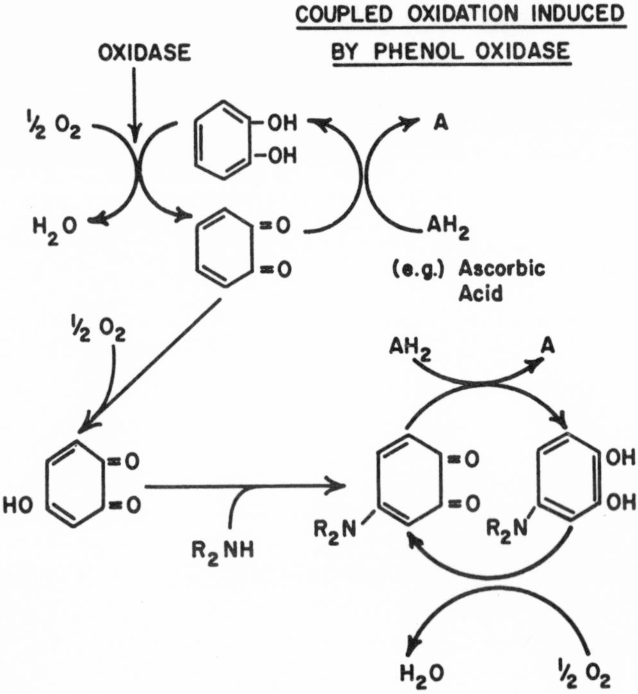

COUPLED OXIDATION INDUCED
OXIDASE
BY PHENOL OXIDASE

$\frac{1}{2}$ O$_2$

OXIDASE

—OH

A

H$_2$O

=O

AH$_2$

=O

(e.g.) Ascorbic
Acid

$\frac{1}{2}$ O$_2$

AH$_2$

A

HO

=O

=O

R$_2$N

=O

=O

R$_2$N

OH

OH

R$_2$NH

H$_2$O

$\frac{1}{2}$ O$_2$

FIGURE 10.—Coupled oxidation induced by phenol oxidase with catechol as substrate. AH$_2$ is a reducing agent and R$_2$NH a secondary amine, such as dimethylamine.

1957; and Mason, 1955), and the resulting substituted quinone can then act as an oxidizing agent for a few amino acids, particularly glycine (Figure 10). Although such reactions may contribute to the metabolism of senescent leaves (Frankenburg, 1950, and Hess, 1958), their importance in ordinary respiration is very doubtful.

Of greater significance to the problem of electron transfer during respiration is the early observation of Kubowitz (1937) that reduced nucleotides can be oxidized by quinones. Wosilait *et al.* (1954) have described an enzyme from peas, quinone reductase, which apparently facilitates this reaction. The following sequence thus provides a possible pathway to O_2 for electrons from a respiratory intermediate:

To decide whether phenol oxidase does in fact function as a terminal oxidase in such a way in the respiration of a particular tissue, several criteria can be applied (Table XV). These will be examined in a later section.

We may note that in preliminary reports Bonner (1955, 1956) has suggested that phenol oxidase may be bound rather tightly to mitochondrial particles from mung bean and other plants and function *in vivo* by transferring electrons from its substrate, not to atmospheric O_2 but to a cytochrome component (see also Sisler and Evans, 1958). Bonner (1957) points out that, although phenol oxidase has long been regarded as a soluble component, association with chloroplasts (e.g., Arnon, 1949) and other particulates has previously been observed (Haskins, 1955). The significance of these observations is not yet clear, but the recent demonstration of coenzyme Q (ubiquinone, Q275) as a component of the particulate succinoxidase and its widespread occurrence in plants (Crane, 1959) is of considerable interest.

Other functions than respiratory ones have been ascribed to phenol oxidase. It has frequently been invoked to explain the utilization of some of the phenolic units which are regarded as lignin precursors (Freudenberg, 1959; Higuchi, 1958). The hydroxylating activity may be important in the production of polyphenols and in flavonol synthesis. What must be at best an incidental role for the enzyme is one associated with the resistance of some plant parts to attack by pathogens (e.g., Johnson and Schaal, 1957). In considering any role for phenol oxidase it should be noted that, although the enzyme is widespread, some plant parts, e.g., barley roots (James, 1953) and pea internodes (Eichenberger and Thimann, 1957), appear to be devoid of the enzyme.

ASCORBIC ACID OXIDASE

Ascorbic acid oxidase was first described from cabbages by Szent Györgyi in 1931 and is now known to be of widespread though not universal distribution in higher plants. Some of the best sources are among the crucifers and cucurbits. It catalyzes the oxidation of ascorbic acid to dehydroascorbic acid, which is fairly stable under acid conditions. There is some evidence that a semiquinone oxidation product, "monodehydroascorbic acid," may be formed as an intermediate:

```
O=C----┐        O=C----┐        O=C----┐
 |      |         |     |         |     |
HOC     |        O—C    O        O=C    |
 ‖      |         ‖     |         |     O
HOC     O        HOC    |        O=C    |
 |      |         |     |         |     |
HC------┘        HC-----┘        HC-----┘
 |               |               |
CHOH            CHOH            CHOH
 |               |               |
CH₂OH           CH₂OH           CH₂OH
```

Ascorbic acid + O_2 → Dehydroascorbic acid + H_2O

The substrate, (L-)ascorbic acid (Vitamin C), is found in trace amounts in many plant tissues and in quite noticeable quantities in some, e.g., citrus fruits. Like the substrates for the phenol oxidases (p. 68), it is present very largely in the reduced form (e.g., Barker and Mapson, 1959). Thus the question of activity of reducing systems is again raised. Although the enzyme has been widely regarded as a soluble oxidase, it is now clear from recent work that an insoluble counterpart exists in some tissues, e.g., in barley seedlings (Butt and Hallaway, 1958; Honda, 1955a; Hansl, 1955) and tobacco callus (Newcomb, 1951). A large fraction of the enzyme activity was found to be associated with the cell-wall fraction, which is normally discarded during preparation of enzymes.

The fact that ionic copper can bring about the oxidation of ascorbate led to early doubts about the existence of the enzyme. It is true that copper ions in plant extracts or experimental solutions are a real hazard in work with ascorbic oxidase, but it is now quite clear that the enzyme is a bona fide member of the club. Butt and Hallaway (1958) have recently provided criteria by which it can be deduced whether ionic copper or the oxidase is responsible for the oxidation of ascorbate when it is added to an extract. The enzymic oxidation, in contrast to that induced by Cu^{++}, is characterized by (a) very rapid turnover of Cu, (b) substrate saturation at 0.004 M, (c) insensitivity to 0.002 M EDTA, and (d) complete inhibition by 0.0001 M diethyldithiocarbamate and hydroxyquinoline. The enzyme has been highly purified from squash (Powers *et al.*, 1944), and the best preparations contained 0.25% copper. It is very sensitive to cyanide and chelating agents for copper, it is only slightly affected by CO, and the affinity for O_2 is rather low (Table XV).

The coexistence of the oxidase and its substrate in plant tissues raises the possibility of their importance in electron transport during respiration. Barker and Mapson (1952) and Mapson (1958) described fluctuations in the intracellular levels of dehydroascorbate and the conversion of added dehydroascorbate to the reduced form which were consistent with the picture that in normal cells the activity of reducing systems keeps the ascorbate in this form. This possibility has been enhanced by the discovery of other enzymes which provide links between known respiratory intermediates and the ascorbic oxidase reaction.

James and his Oxford group, working with (soluble) barley extracts, provided evidence that O_2 uptake in the presence of ascorbate could be augmented by the addition of substrates such as lactate for which dehydrogenases were present (James *et al.*, 1944; James and Cragg, 1943). Waygood (1950), with wheat, was able to show that the O_2 uptake in the presence of malic acid or ethanol and DPN exceeded that for the total oxidation of the ascorbate alone. He recognized the participation of other components in the oxidation systems. The nature of these links has become clearer during the past few years.

Oxidation systems involving -SH compounds as intermediates. The interrelations between the tripeptide glutathione and the ascorbate system (see Mapson, 1958) became clearer when it was shown that many plant extracts contained an enzyme (dehydroascorbate reductase) which transferred hydrogen from glutathione (GSH) to dehydroascorbic acid. In a mixture containing ascorbic oxidase, dehydroascorbate reductase, glutathione, and ascorbate, the ascorbate was maintained in the reduced form until the GSH was exhausted.

Great interest attached to the subsequent demonstrations by Mapson and Goddard (1951) and Conn and Vennesland (1951) of an enzyme which provided a direct link between the ascorbate couple and respiratory intermediates reducing TPN. This enzyme, TPNH-glutathione reductase, found originally in peas and wheat germ, has since been shown to be widespread in plants (Anderson *et al.*, 1952; Laudi, 1955; see Mapson's review). Enzyme activity can be measured by following the disappearance of the absorption band at 340 mμ or by titrimetric determination of the product GSH. In the presence of a suitable substrate and its dehydrogenase, electrons can be transferred, through the sequence below, to atmospheric O_2 through the agency of ascorbic oxidase as the terminal enzyme (AA and DHA are ascorbate and dehydroascorbate, respectively). Such a sequence can be regarded as a soluble TPNH- or DPNH-oxidase (Marrè and Servattez, 1958), but it also may be found associated with mitochondria (Marrè and Laudi, 1956). Cystine may play a similar role in linking DPNH to the ascorbic oxidase (Romano and Nickerson, 1956).

A different type of link has been demonstrated between DPNH and the ascorbate system. Beevers (1954) and also Nason *et al.* (1954) described similar enzymes in higher plant extracts which are able to transfer electrons from DPNH to an intermediate product of ascorbic acid oxidation by its oxidase but not to dehydroascorbate. The cucumber enzyme was

Dehydro-genase	GSSG reductase	DHA reductase	Ascorbic oxidase

Substrate H_2 e.g., Glucose-6-P — TPN — GSH — DHA — H_2O

Oxidized substrate 6-P-Gluconic acid — TPNH — GSSG — AA — $\frac{1}{2}O_2$

extremely sensitive to -SH reagents. Nason showed that an unstable product of ascorbate oxidation was the H acceptor in this system. Since the only other oxidants which could generate the acceptor from ascorbate were ones which induced removal of single electrons, it was concluded that the unstable product was a semiquinone "monodehydroascorbic acid." Matthews (1951) had provided earlier evidence that such a product was involved in a cyanide-insensitive ascorbate system. It should be emphasized that the systems studied by Beevers (and by Nason)—Bonner's statement in his 1957 review to the contrary notwithstanding—are completely inhibited by cyanide; there is no doubt that ascorbic acid oxidase is the terminal step in the transfer. Similar systems of pyridine nucleotide oxidation have been studied more recently by Hackett (1958) using potato, Fujimura and Ikeda (1957) using various leaves, and Marrè and Laudi (1957) using peas.

GLYCOLIC ACID OXIDASE

Another enzyme which catalyzes the direct oxidation of its substrate by molecular O_2 is α-hydroxy acid or glycolic acid oxidase. This oxidase was described first by Burris' group in Wisconsin (Claggett et al., 1949). Crude extracts from a variety of green tissues oxidized glycolic and lactic acids; the enzyme was not found in roots and only in very small amounts in etiolated parts. When nongreen tissues were exposed to light, the appearance of glycolic oxidase coincided with the greening and beginning photosynthesis of the tissue (Tolbert and Burris, 1950; Noll and Burris, 1954). It was shown that the initial product of glycolate oxidation was glyoxylate, which was further oxidized. When lactate was the substrate, the oxidation rate was only one-third that of glycolate, and the product was pyruvate. The enzyme was not inhibited by metal complexing reagents but was inhibited by iodoacetate; it was shown to be a flavoprotein reducing O_2 to H_2O_2. Dichlorophenol-indophenol can substitute for O_2 as the electron acceptor, and the enzyme can thus behave as a glycolic dehydrogenase (see also Franke et al., 1956).

Some of the subsequent work with this enzyme has centered on the activation by light, on possible relationships to pigment development, and to photosynthesis in which glycolate is an early by-product. Kolesnikov (1954, 1956, 1957) confirmed the wide distribution of enzyme in green plant parts and its resistance to cyanide, azide, and diethyldithiocarbamate. He provided evidence that the prosthetic group was flavin mononucleotide. There was some indication that the activity of the enzyme was induced by its substrate, but Mothes and Wagner (1957) found no such indication in roots, although high activity was developed when they were allowed to become green.

From the start it was recognized that secondary oxidations of glyoxylate were induced in the crude systems (Tolbert et al., 1949). These have now been further clarified by Kenten and Mann (1952a,b) and particularly by Zelitch and Ochoa (1953) and Zelitch (1953). The primary reaction, catalyzed by the enzyme, is Reaction 1:

$$\text{Glycolate} + O_2 \rightarrow \text{Glyoxylate} + H_2O_2 \qquad (1)$$

$$H_2O_2 \rightarrow H_2O + \tfrac{1}{2}O_2 \qquad (2)$$

$$\textit{Over all:} \ \text{Glycolate} + \tfrac{1}{2}O_2 \rightarrow \text{Glyoxylate} + H_2O \qquad (3)$$

If sufficient catalase is present, the H_2O_2 is decomposed (Reaction 2), and the over-all reaction becomes that in Reaction 3. If H_2O_2 is not removed, it induces a nonenzymatic oxidation of glyoxylate to formate and CO_2. Zelitch and Ochoa (1953) purified the oxidase from spinach extensively and showed conclusively that flavin mononucleotide was the specific prosthetic group which was easily dissociated from the enzyme protein. They also showed that enzyme systems capable of reducing glyoxylate were present, which accounted for the sustained O_2 uptake in crude systems which had been observed earlier. A glyoxylic acid reductase was isolated, which was able to transfer electrons from reduced pyridine nucleotides to glyoxylic acid. This enzyme has been crystallized by Zelitch (1955), and shown to oxidize DPNH exclusively. By the use of suitable substrates and dehydrogenases, linked systems were reconstructed in which respiratory intermediates were oxidized by atmospheric O_2 according to the following sequences:

Frigerio and Harbury (1958) have recently crystallized glycolic oxidase from spinach and have examined the physical properties of the enzyme. The O_2 affinity of the enzyme is apparently low (O_2 uptake in pure O_2 was 4.5 times that in air). We may note that this enzyme is the first oxidase to be crystallized, and it is thus possible to construct a soluble oxidizing system of completely purified and known components. The possible importance of such a system in plant respiration will be examined later. We will note for the present its cyanide resistance and also the fact that more or less specific inhibitors have been described (Zelitch, 1957). It will be recalled that Tewfik and Stumpf (1951), and more extensively Gibbs (1954), showed that various sugar phosphates were oxidized by a soluble enzyme system from peas. The O_2 uptake was not inhibited by cyanide and was stimulated by addition of flavins. It seems possible that the glycolic oxidase–glyoxylic reductase system may have been responsible for the final stages of electron transfer to O_2.

PEROXIDASE AND CATALASE

The activities of peroxidase and catalase have been the sub-ject of thorough reviews; those of Theorell (1951), Chance (1951), and Mason (1955) should be consulted. Hill and Har-tree (1953) have provided a particularly valuable discussion in their review on haematin compounds in plants.

Theorell states that "peroxidase is everywhere in higher plants." The soluble enzyme (the "indirect oxidase" of Ons-low, 1931) can induce the oxidation of a variety of phenols and amines when H_2O_2 is provided as the electron acceptor. We may note that this is another enzyme for which a higher plant is known as the major source—horse-radish peroxidase has been intensively studied. It has been crystallized from this source (see Theorell) and more recently from wheat germ (Tagawa et al., 1959). A great deal of work has been done on the mechanism of the peroxidase reaction, which is still not completely resolved, and on the chemistry of the enzyme. What is possibly of importance in the respiration of plants is the utilization by peroxidase of H_2O_2 (produced by the flavo-protein oxidases) in the induced oxidation of other cellular metabolites.

Catalase is usually regarded as a detoxifying agent for H_2O_2 on account of its universal occurrence in aerobic organisms and its extremely efficient breakdown of its substrate to H_2O and O_2. The ability of added catalase to prevent an enzymatic oxidation is frequently used as proof that a peroxidase en-zyme is involved, although the H_2O_2 might be undetectable by chemical means.

$$2 H_2O_2 \xrightarrow{\text{Catalase}} 2 H_2O + O_2 \qquad (1)$$

$$AH_2 + H_2O_2 \xrightarrow{\text{Peroxidase}} 2 H_2O + A \qquad (2)$$

Since catalase destroys the substrate (Reaction 1) for peroxi-dase (Reaction 2), it might be thought that peroxidase ac-tivity in a cell equipped with both soluble enzymes would be impossible. However, it is clear from Chance's work (1951) that extremely low levels of hydrogen peroxide are required for peroxidase activity, and in some systems, indeed (see below), hydrogen peroxide need not be added since it is apparently generated continuously during the oxidation. Furthermore, it has been clear since the work of Keilin and Hartree (1936) and Chance (1951) that at low levels of H_2O_2 (10^{-9} M) catalase itself induces the oxidation of, for example, ethanol. Waygood and MacLachlan (1956) have induced the oxidation of IAA by catalase. It is now felt that the "peroxidative" activity of catalase (Reaction 2) rather than its "catalatic" activity (Reaction 1) may be of greater importance *in vivo*, although its potential detoxifying action is not to be denied.

In the presence of H_2O_2, added from without, or internally generated, e.g., by glycolic oxidase and its substrate, a variety of oxidations can be induced by plant saps containing peroxidase. In the coupled system the peroxidase substrate is, in effect, oxidized by atmospheric O_2, which is introduced into H_2O_2 by the flavoprotein. Of even greater interest are reactions catalyzed by the peroxidase in which no source of H_2O_2 is provided and a purely oxidative activity with continued O_2 uptake (in the absence of a flavoprotein) is observed. The oxidation of dihydroxyfumaric acid (Theorell, 1951) was the first example of this:

$$AH_2 + \tfrac{1}{2}O_2 \xrightarrow{\text{Peroxidase, } Mn^{++}\text{Phenol}} A + H_2O, \qquad (3)$$

where AH_2 is dihydroxyfumaric acid, oxalacetic acid, indoleacetic acid, PNH, etc.

More recently, the Rothamstead group (Kenten and Mann, 1953) have demonstrated the oxidation of Mn^{++} by peroxidase preparations. In the presence of Mn^{++} and a phenol such as resorcinol (but without added H_2O_2) the oxidation of a variety of substances was induced (Kenten and Mann, 1953; Kenten, 1953). O_2 uptake was measured manometrically. Phenylacetaldehyde, tryptophan, and acids such as oxalacetic and ketomalic were some of the reductants. The enzyme apparently acts both as an oxidase and a peroxidase in the reaction. It is now clear that similar, but perhaps not identical, reactions are involved in extracts with indoleacetic acid oxidase activity (Kenten, 1954; Waygood *et al.*, 1956). MacLachlan and Waygood (1956) have made detailed suggestions about the reaction mechanism. The critical and apparently unsettled question is the mechanism of the origin of the internally generated H_2O_2.

The significance of such induced oxidations, if indeed they occur *in vivo*, is not yet established. A similar view must at present be taken of reactions which appear to be of greater potential importance to the respiratory process, namely, the induced oxidation of pyridine nucleotides by peroxidase systems. Conn *et al.* (1952) showed that peroxidase was involved in the oxidation of TPNH brought about by wheat-germ extracts, and a similar but not identical system was studied by Humphreys (1955). More recently Stern and Johnston (1957) isolated particles (heavier than mitochondria) from viable wheat embryos which seemed to combine the activities reported by Conn *et al.* and Humphreys. Conn and Seki (1957) had previously described a peroxidase activity associated with mitochondrial particles.

Akazawa and Conn (1958) recently demonstrated a vigorous oxidation of both TPNH and DPNH by crystalline horseradish peroxidase in the presence of catalytic amounts of Mn^{++} and a monohydric phenol. Exogenous H_2O_2 was not required, but its internal generation and participation in the reaction could be inferred from the inhibition of O_2 uptake by catalase. The ineffectiveness of added H_2O_2 has been noticed in at least two other peroxidase systems. Stumpf's (1956) saturated fatty acid peroxidase (which specifically oxidizes long-chain saturated fatty acids to aldehydes and CO_2) is one of these; it thrives on H_2O_2 generated by flavoprotein enzymes and is not, incidentally, inhibited by catalase. Again Yamada and Oota (1958) found that rice extracts induced the oxidation of ferrous ion in a peroxidase-like action in the absence of added H_2O_2.

In looking for physiological roles for these enzymes, their sensitivity to cyanide and azide and resistance to CO (Table XV) should be borne in mind. It should be pointed out, however, that when peroxidase was acting oxidatively on dihydroxyfumarate (Theorell, 1951) the reaction was inhibited by

CO and, furthermore, the inhibition was reversed by light. Since this property is an important criterion for the participation of cytochrome oxidase, it would be of interest to know whether the more recently described oxidative systems (especially those of Kenten and of Conn) were similarly sensitive to CO.

Finally, we may note that it has been suggested that peroxidase-catalyzed reactions are important in lignin biogenesis (Freudenberg, 1959; Siegel, 1953; Higuchi, 1957). Jensen (1955) claims on the basis of histochemical evidence that IAA induces the formation of peroxidase in vascular tissues.

MISCELLANEOUS OXIDASES

Lipoxidase. This is an enzyme of limited distribution whose significance is not understood (for a review see Holman and Bergstrom, 1951). It oxidizes unsaturated fatty acids such as linolenic to corresponding hydroperoxides. In those seedlings where it occurs the oxidation of its substrate may account for much of the O_2 uptake when breis or extracts are prepared (Fritz and Beevers, 1955b). Since the coupled oxidation of various carotenoids, tocopherol, and dyes can also be induced— the mechanism is not understood (Mason, 1955)—a logical, though on the face of it unlikely, possibility must be entertained (Fritz and Beevers, 1955b) that lipoxidase is an agent through which electrons from respiratory substrates are funneled to atmospheric O_2. Fortunately, the lipoxidase reaction is unusual in that oxygen from the atmosphere combines with the substrate, and this allows a direct test of the hypothesis that it is involved in normal respiratory uptake. Fritz *et al.* (1958) showed that only a very small amount of O_2 was actually chemically incorporated into the tissue during rapid respiration of corn seedlings. We have therefore now some experimental basis for regarding lipoxidase as unlikely to be of respiratory significance, even in those tissues which contain the enzyme.

Amine oxidase. The Rothamstead group have investigated the ability of extracts from plants to oxidize a variety of amines by an enzyme distinct from peroxidase (Mann, 1955).

The enzyme has been extensively purified and can oxidize mono- and diamines as well as D- and L-lysine. Cyanide and diethyldithiocarbamate inhibit O_2 consumption, and small amounts of copper and manganese were present in the final preparations. H_2O_2 is produced during the oxidation. No evidence of cyclic oxidation and reduction of the substrate has been demonstrated, which would make the enzyme of interest in respiratory oxidations, but secondary oxidations may be induced by the H_2O_2.

THE CYTOCHROME OXIDASE SYSTEM

The cytochromes are a group of related proteins with iron porphyrin prosthetic groups firmly attached. When the iron in the porphyrin is converted into the reduced (Fe^{++}) condition, the cytochromes show characteristic increases in the absorption of some of the visible light waves. This feature made possible their early recognition in very diverse cell types by MacMunn (1885) and more clearly and extensively by Keilin (1925), to whom a great deal of the present understanding of these important agents is due. A recent authoritative review of cytochromes in plants is that by Hartree (1957).

The characteristic 4-banded absorption spectrum (observed after exposure of the living cells to dithionite to reduce the cytochromes and cooling to intensify the bands) was eventually ascribed to three separate cytochromes, a, b, and c. Each of these has a prominent absorption band in the region of 550 mμ–600 mμ (α band) and a second band (γ or Soret band) in the 415–450 mμ region. In addition, cytochromes b and c have β bands between 520 and 530 mμ. The band at 603.5 was later shown to be due to two closely connected components, cytochromes a and a_3 (Table XI).

TABLE XI
ABSORPTION BANDS OF SPECTRA OF LIVING TISSUES ASCRIBABLE TO CYTOCHROMES

Wave length	603.5	564	549	519
Cytochrome	a(+a_3) (α band)	b (α band)	c (α band)	b (β band)

Keilin was able to show (by increases in the intensity of the absorption bands) that the cytochromes were converted into the reduced form when the cells were deprived of O_2 and that they became oxidized (bands disappeared) when they were subsequently aerated. By means of inhibitors such as CO and azide it was established that only cytochrome a_3 was autoxidizable, and it was as a result of this autoxidation that the coupled oxidation of the other pigments was brought about. From spectroscopic experiments such as these, carried out first with yeast suspensions (in which the absorption bands are relatively intense), and the knowledge at hand about effects of the inhibitors on respiratory oxygen uptake, the cytochrome chain became firmly established as the agency whereby O_2 was absorbed in cellular respiration. Cytochrome a and the closely associated and spectroscopically similar a_3 together represent the final steps in the chain, and a_3 may be regarded as the cytochrome oxidase. Cytochrome c with the prominent α band in the region of 550 mμ is the immediate reductant for cytochrome a, and this in turn can accept electrons from the reduced cytochrome b. A tremendous amount of subsequent work has been carried out on the separation of these cytochromes and others more recently discovered, their interplay, and their connections with respiratory substrates and flavoproteins in extracted oxidation systems. The changing phases in the development of this work and the past and present unresolved differences in interpretation can be followed in the *Annual Review of Biochemistry* over the past twenty years.

After Keilin's demonstration of cytochrome bands in some plant materials, other observers, notably Okunuki, were able to extend the list. Working with pollen grains, Okunuki (1939) demonstrated CO inhibition of cytochrome oxidation *in vivo* and its reversibility by light. More recently Bhagvat and Hill (1951), Lundegårdh (1953, 1954, 1959), and Martin and Morton (1957) have described cytochrome absorption bands and their changing intensities in aerobic and anaerobic conditions. It should not be thought, however, that it is a simple matter to "see" a piece of plant material respiring by simply interposing it between a light source and a spectro-

scope and observing dramatic changes in the intensity of the
α bands when it is intermittently exposed to air and N_2. Hill
and Hartree, themselves practiced in the art, point out that
"the visual observation of spectrum bands of cytochrome in
plant tissues, where they are present only at low concentration
(c. 5% of that in yeast) requires no little experience." The interference, both by other haem and nonhaem pigments, ag-
gravates the problem of interpreting the observed spectrum.
In green leaves, of course, the strong light absorption by the
pigments makes it impossible to observe the cytochrome bands
directly. Some of the newer optical devices and recorders, notably those of Lundegårdh (1956), Chance (1957), Yocum and
Hackett (1957), and Martin and Morton (1957), have provided
valuable data from intact (nongreen) materials and incidentally have raised new problems in interpretation. What is clear
from this recent work is that more or less well-defined bands
coinciding in position with those of the classical spectrum
can be shown to be present in tissues such as onion, silver beet,
wheat roots, and various aroid spadices (see p. 110). Those of
the wheat roots have received the most intensive study by
Lundegårdh. Since some of the interpretations are matters of
debate, the experiments will not be discussed in detail and the
reader is referred to the thoughtful and critical appraisal recently provided by Smith and Chance (1958).

In most of the work with intact tissues the aim is to observe
the absorption peaks of the reduced cytochrome components
by depriving the system of O_2 or by inhibiting with CN, and
to compare the resulting spectrum with the aerated condition.
Difference spectra which are derived by subtracting the two
curves so obtained sometimes show clear peaks corresponding
to known cytochromes (Figure 11). However, nonspecific optical effects, such as general increases in absorption on transfer
to N_2, interference by other pigments such as flavoprotein
and peroxidase, CN complexes with strong absorption bands,
and O_2 effects on pigments not concerned with respiration,
are only some of the hazards besetting interpretation. These
considerations add to the difficulties of determining (by observing the rates of appearance and disappearance of the vari-

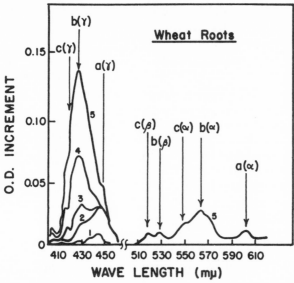

FIGURE 11.—Difference spectra obtained from living wheat roots. Curves 1, 2, 3, 4, and 5 show progressive changes in the reduction of the various components after 1, 4, 7, 13, and 23 minutes of anaerobiosis in succinate (after Lundegårdh, 1953).

ous peaks on transfer to and from N_2) the order in which the various components occur in the electron-transfer sequence in the intact tissue. However, from experiments such as those illustrated in Figure 11, Lundegårdh (1953) has calculated the times for reduction of cytochromes b, c, and a and has shown that a is more rapidly reduced than c and that b is the last to become reduced on depriving wheat roots of O_2. All are rapidly reoxidized when air is admitted.

Much of the interpretation is necessarily colored by what has been established in yeast; and while there is evidence of uniformity, there are appearing in the literature a disturbing number of new bands whose assignation to the "normal" cytochromes is difficult or impossible. (The multiplicity of the cytochromes already described and their overlapping absorption spectra can be seen in Hartree's 1957 review.) The more tissues which are examined by different instruments, the greater, for the present at least, these puzzles in interpretation become. Some workers apparently now prefer not to assign the absorption bands to any particular component but to refer to them by wave length only. This is a symptom of open-mindedness about identification of the pigments and the order in which they are aligned in electron transfer *in vivo*, and emphasizes that the issues are far from settled.

The plant tissue with the most striking cytochrome absorption bands is the aroid spadix (Bonner and Yocum, 1956; Hackett, 1957; Bendall and Hill, 1956), which is distinguished by other characteristics, namely, its extremely high but CN-resistant respiratory rate (pp. 108 ff.). The total cytochrome haem concentration in English *Arum* and the skunk-cabbage flower parts is close to that observed in the yeasts, and a very noticeable component, in addition to the usual cytochromes, is an autoxidizable cytochrome b_7, with absorption bands at about 560 mμ and 529 mμ; the significance of this will be discussed later.

A much larger number of plants have yielded direct evidence of the presence of the cytochrome system in enzyme assays than have provided the unequivocal classical 4-banded absorption spectrum of Keilin. Bhagvat and Hill (1951) carried out pioneering investigations which demonstrated the capacity of a variety of plant extracts to bring about a cytochrome-stimulated oxidation of succinate. These authors, in contrast to previous workers on plant oxidases, examined the insoluble or sedimented fraction of homogenates rather than the supernatant solution, and their success in showing that the cytochrome system was attached to insoluble particles marked the beginning of a new chapter in the study of plant respiration. Goddard's (1944) successful isolation of cytochrome c from wheat germ is another important landmark which also emphasized the need for looking further than the soluble oxidases for an understanding of plant respiration.

The manometric estimation of cytochrome oxidase activity has been widely used. In this method an artificial donor, AH_2, reduces spontaneously and rapidly the oxidized cytochrome c generated by the enzyme (Figure 9), and a cyclic system with the cytochrome c acting catalytically is maintained as follows:

$$AH_2 \rightarrow \quad 2\,Cyt\,c\,Fe^{+++} \leftarrow \quad \rightarrow 2\,Cyt\,oxidase\,Fe^{++} \rightarrow \quad \tfrac{1}{2}O_2$$
$$A \leftarrow \quad 2\,Cyt\,c\,Fe^{++} \quad 2\,Cyt\,oxidase\,Fe^{+++} \leftarrow \quad H_2O$$
$$2H^+ \text{-----------------------------------}$$

Ascorbic acid, hydroquinone, and paraphenylenediamine are the usual reductants, but each of these has its disadvantages (Hill and Hartree, 1953; Simon, 1958). The direct spectrophotometric demonstration of the oxidation of added cytochrome c (Fe^{++}) by observing the decrease in absorbance at 550 mμ is a more satisfactory and sensitive method of measuring cytochrome oxidase activity (Figure 12).

Cytochrome oxidase has now been detected in a large number of species by such methods. Webster's (1952) report alone records activity from 54 different plants. In general, the cytochrome oxidase is considerably less robust and vigorous than the soluble oxidases from the same tissue, and pre-

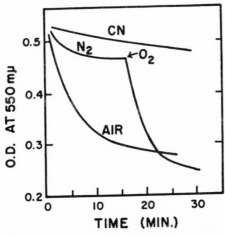

FIGURE 12.—Oxidation of reduced cytochrome c by a mitochondrial preparation from potato. The enzyme was added at time 0. Note that oxidation is prevented by cyanide (0.0001 M) and by anaerobic conditions (after Hackett, 1956).

cautions must be taken to guard against acid conditions, rises in temperature, and the appearance of toxic quinones. Smith and Chance (1958) discuss the various reasons why less than maximal values are usually recorded in assays of the oxidases. Two features which have not been generally recognized are that cytochrome c at high concentrations and other native proteins are inhibitory.

The first successful isolation of mitochondria from higher plants with succinoxidase activity by Millerd *et al.* (1951) and the subsequent general localization of this activity (see Goddard and Meeuse, 1950; Hackett, 1955) have made it clear that the insoluble particles of Bhagvat and Hill which oxidized succinate and cytochrome c were derived from mitochondria. These latter authors used a grinding medium of low tonicity, whereas a sucrose concentration of about 0.25–0.5 M is required if the mitochondria are to remain intact. There have been many subsequent reports of succinate oxidation by plant mitochondria (Chapter 3), and the presence of the cytochrome oxidase system can be directly inferred from these. In some preparations the ability to oxidize added cytochrome c has been directly demonstrated (e.g., Chow and Biale, 1957). As shown in Table XII, much higher "yields" of cytochrome oxidase can frequently be obtained by treating the mitochondria with digitonin (Simon, 1958). This agent apparently induces a physical change which exposes more of the internal cytochrome oxidase to the cytochrome c and reductant added from outside. In contrast to the co-ordinated activity of the TCA-cycle enzymes, cytochrome oxidase activity is retained after mitochondrial rupture and is supposed to be part of the outer mitochondrial membrane. However, experiments with lecithinase (Goodwin and Waygood, 1954) indicate that, as in the mammalian system, some minimal structural arrangement is required even for cytochrome oxidase activity. Considerable progress has been made in isolating individual cytochromes and other components of the electron-transport chain from mammalian mitochondria. Comparable work in plants is also beginning. Cytochrome c is fairly readily lost from maltreated mitochondria and can be re-

TABLE XII

EFFECT OF DIGITONIN TREATMENT ON MITOCHONDRIAL CYTOCHROME OXIDASE

(SIMON, 1958)

TREATMENT	CYTOCHROME OXIDASE (μl. O_2/hr./g wet wt.)		
	Control	Digitonin-Treated	Ratio: Treated/Control
Stem:			
Potato tuber	2.0	51	25
Roots:			
Swede	3.5	38	11
Carrot	0.8	9.8	12
Beetroot	3.5	24	7
Leek	23	64	3
Fruits:			
Marrow	2.4	80	33
Pear	0.6	31	52
Leaves:			
Celery petiole	6.0	110	18
Onion bulb	1.2	53	44
Cabbage bud	10	120	12
Seedlings:			
Phaseolus hypocotyl (5 day)	4.7	130	28
Ricinus endosperm (6 day)	88	540	6
Fungus:			
Mushroom stipe	6.4	160	25

covered in the supernatant solution. Evans' group have prepared "soluble" forms of cytochrome oxidase from particles
of soybean and tobacco roots (Miller *et al.*, 1958), and a weak
DPNH-oxidase has been separated from mitochondria by
Humphreys and Conn (1956).

The fact that the cytochrome oxidase and linked electron-
donating systems are confined, in most preparations, to the
mitochondria (see Chapter 6) has made possible their spectroscopic examination in a concentrated form *in vitro*. Some

TABLE XIII

SPECTROSCOPIC DEMONSTRATION OF CYTOCHROME COMPONENTS IN
FRACTIONATED EXTRACTS OF NONGREEN PLANT PARTS

Material	Component	Cytochromes Present	Authors
Wheat roots	Mitochondria	a_3, b, c	Lundegårdh, 1958
	Microsomes	c, c_1, b_3	
	Supernatant	c, c_1 (plus peroxidase and flavoprotein)	
Silver-beet petiole and wheat roots	Mitochondria	a, a_3, b, c, c_1	Martin and Morton, 1957
	Microsomes	b_3	Martin and Morton, 1957
Cauliflower buds	"Medium particles"	a, b_3, c(c_1)	Crane, 1957
	"Light particles"	b_3	
Avocado	Cytoplasmic particles	c	Chow and Biale, 1957
Aroid spadix	Mitochondria	a, b, b_7, c	Several, see text

representative results are shown in Table XIII. Difference
spectra of aerobic and anaerobic mitochondria (Figure 14)
have provided the bases for the conclusions that the cytochromes indicated are present in the preparations. Values for
microsomes and light particles are included to emphasize that
one of the cytochromes, b_3, with absorption bands at 560 mμ
(α) and 425 mμ (γ), is concentrated in these particles. Although cytochrome c is occasionally found in the supernate, it
is likely that in the intact cell it is exclusively associated with
the mitochondria.

A few years ago the evidence for the existence of cytochrome oxidase in plants was meager, and functioning mitochondria had still to be isolated from them. Now it is abun-
dantly clear that the enzyme and its substrate are widely
distributed and apparently universal in higher plant tissues.
It is no longer a matter for surprise that a plant tissue should
yield functioning mitochondria with the cytochrome system
intact; on the contrary, a claim that a particular plant tissue

was without this equipment would now be regarded with suspicion.

The probable importance of this sequence in cellular respiration is of course further enhanced by the existence of links, again in the mitochondria, which connect the cytochromes to the dehydrogenation of respiratory intermediates.

ELECTRON TRANSFER TO THE CYTOCHROMES

When substrates of the TCA cycle are being oxidized by plant mitochondria, the cytochrome system provides the final link with O_2. In only a few cases is the oxidation rate of individual acids stimulated by exogenous cytochrome c; the intact mitochondria are usually self-sufficient in this regard. However, the mitochondria can bring about the oxidation of added cytochrome c (Fe^{++}) (e.g., Chow and Biale, 1957; Crane, 1957), and if the mitochondria are damaged, striking stimulations of substrate oxidation may be induced (Bhagvat and Hill, 1951). The sensitivity of O_2 uptake to cyanide and to a group of compounds which block the transfer of electrons between cytochromes b and c and between DPNH and cytochrome c (e.g., antimycin A, 2,3-dimercaptopropanol [BAL]) further supports the importance of the cytochrome chain. Other experimental evidence includes the appearance of the reduced cytochrome bands when substrate is supplied and the effects of inhibitors on the spectral changes (Figure 14).

Data so obtained, from a variety of plant mitochondria, have been assembled in Table XIV. It will be seen that all of the observations are accommodated in the sequence at the head of the table, and therefore they support the view that electron transfer actually occurs along such a pathway. The sequence was not, of course, proposed originally to fit these observations from higher plants; similar and much more extensive ones from yeasts and from mammalian particulates have provided the basis for this and other present-day pictures of electron transport. It should not be thought that the scheme is not subject to further modifications as new facts come to light or that all authorities agree on the participation or plac-

TABLE XIV

MODEL FOR ELECTRON TRANSPORT AND EVIDENCE FOR ITS
OPERATION IN PLANT MITOCHONDRIA

$$\text{Substrate} \rightarrow \text{DPN} \rightarrow \text{FP} \rightarrow \text{Cyt. b} \rightarrow \text{ASC} \rightarrow \text{Cyt. } c_1 \rightarrow$$

with Dye branching above FP, and:

$$\text{Cyt. c} \rightarrow \text{Cyt. a} \rightarrow \text{Cyt. } a_3 \rightarrow O_2$$

$$\text{Succinate} \rightarrow \text{SD} \rule{}{}$$

where FP is the flavoprotein component of DPNH $\rightarrow$ Cyt. c reductase
ASC is the antimycin-sensitive component (Slater factor)
SD is the succinic dehydrogenase flavoprotein

Span	Properties	Authors
Substrate $\rightarrow O_2$	TCA-cycle acids	Many, see text
Substrate $\rightarrow$ DPN	Citric + malic acids	Many, see text
DPNH $\rightarrow O_2$	FAD-stimulated	Howard and Yamaguchi, 1957
"	CN-sensitive, antimycin-sensitive	Crane, 1957
DPNH $\rightarrow$ ASC $\rightarrow O_2$	Stimulated by cyt. c	Hackett, 1956
DPNH $\rightarrow$ Cyt. b, c, c_1, a	Appearance of reduced bands	Martin and Morton, 1956
Cyt. c $\rightarrow O_2$	CN-sensitive	Crane, 1957; Hackett, 1956; Chow and Biale, 1957
DPNH $\rightarrow$ Cyt. c		Hackett, 1956; Crane, 1957; Biale, et al., 1957
Succinate $\rightarrow O_2$	Antimycin-sensitive	Many
Succinate $\rightarrow$ Cyt. b, c, a		Martin and Morton, 1956, 1957
Succinate $\rightarrow$ Cyt. c	Antimycin-sensitive; SN 5949* inhibits	Sisler and Evans, 1959
DPNH $\rightarrow$ Dye	Diaphorase; antimycin-insensitive	Crane, 1957; Hackett, 1956

* 2-Hydroxy-3-(2-methyloctyl)-1,4-naphthoquinone.

ing of each of the components. The fluid condition of the field is brought out by recent reviews by Mahler (1957) and Slater (1958).

Whatever be the final disposition of the individual components, it must of course be one which does not violate observations of the kind listed in Table XIV. These observations establish beyond doubt that oxidation of DPNH and TCA intermediates by the mitochondria occurs by a step-wise sequence including flavoprotein and cytochrome components. Further, insofar as the major oxidative mechanism in carbohydrate breakdown is the TCA cycle, also confined to the mitochondria, it would seem an inevitable conclusion that cytochrome oxidase is the major terminal oxidase in plant respiration.

It should be emphasized that enzymes catalyzing the transfer of electrons from reduced nucleotides to cytochrome c or to dyes are by no means confined to mitochondria. Thus a variety of soluble diaphorases and cytochrome c reductases have been described, and similar enzymes are present in chloroplasts. The significance of such enzymes in respiration is in some doubt for the following reasons:

a. Recent work indicates that diaphorase activity may be more correctly regarded as lipoyl dehydrogenase (Massey, 1960).

b. There is some doubt as to whether cytochrome c reductase or the soluble reductases exist as such in the cell and could effectively channel reducing equivalents to the cytochrome oxidase.

THE PARTICIPATION OF OXIDASES IN PLANT RESPIRATION

We have now surveyed the various oxidases in plants and the ways in which they can co-operate with dehydrogenases and carriers to bring about the oxidation of respiratory intermediates.

The question now presents itself: Which, if any, of the known systems are in fact utilized by the living plant cell in its respiration? Do the various systems for the oxidation of the reduced nucleotides perhaps compete on even terms for the substrate—in which case the pattern of distribution of the various enzymes and their relative activities would be a determining factor—or are there more subtle reasons why one or another of the oxidases is all-important?

We should recognize at once that more than one oxidase

can be extracted from each plant tissue. For example, peroxidase has been found in almost every plant tissue examined, and many of these plant tissues are known to contain phenol oxidases and ascorbic oxidase as well. White potato, for example, has been shown to contain phenol oxidase, ascorbic oxidase, peroxidase, and cytochrome oxidase, and in green parts it presumably has glycolic oxidase in addition. Spinach leaves and corn embryos are other tissues which contain at least four oxidases. It should also be emphasized that frequently the "capacity" of each of several possible oxidases extracted from a tissue by far exceeds the actual rate of respiratory O_2 uptake of the material from which they were derived. For example, it has been shown that the ascorbic oxidase in a given weight of barley roots is sufficient to bring about a rate of O_2 uptake some 40 times greater than that actually observed, and the phenol oxidase from potatoes and apples is even more active. Frequently the activity of the soluble oxidases is much higher than that of cytochrome oxidase, but there is now an impressive number of tissues from which sufficient cytochrome oxidase can be extracted to make it credible that all of the electron transfer occurs through it (Goddard and Stafford, 1954; Webster, 1954; Fritz and Beevers, 1955a; Honda, 1957; Simon, 1958; Sisler and Evans, 1959)—and this in spite of the difficulties of assay of the enzyme (Smith and Chance, 1958). On the count of adequacy of catalytic capacity, then, the difficulty is not one of finding qualified candidates; the question is rather how some of the more boisterous contenders are kept in check.

A good deal of experimental work aimed at finding which are the functional oxidases in plants has been carried out in the past twenty years. In most of this, the method has been to see whether the respiratory O_2 uptake of a slice of tissue responds to a specific change in the environment in the same way as one of the isolated oxidases is known to do *in vitro*. The properties of the oxidases outlined in Table XV have been made use of in this way. As Hill and Hartree (1953) point out, it would seem at first sight an easy matter to dispose of this question by a few appropriate inhibitor experi-

TABLE XV

IMPORTANT PROPERTIES OF ENZYMES WHICH MIGHT FUNCTION
AS TERMINAL OXIDASES

	Phenol Oxidase	Ascorbic Acid Oxidase	Glycolic Oxidase	Peroxidase (Oxidase Function)	Cytochrome Oxidase
Active center	Cu^{++}	Cu^{++}	FMN*	Fe^{++}	Fe^{++}
CN inhibition	+	+	−	+	+
O_2 affinity	$1.3 \times 10^{-5} M$	$1.5 \times 10^{-4} M$	$ca.\ 10^{-4} M$	(?)	$4.5 \times 10^{-6} M$
CO inhibition	+	Slight (−)	−	(?)	+
Light-reversal	−	−	−	(?)	+

* Flavin mononucleotide.

ments, but in fact the disposal has not been at all swift and painless. Difficulties common to all inhibitor experiments (Hartree, 1957) make positive and quantitative deductions difficult. Nevertheless, it is primarily on this basis that present-day assessments are made.

Cyanide and azide sensitivity. The ability of cyanide and azide at concentrations of about 0.001 M to bring about inhibition of O_2 uptake is usually used as a criterion for the participation of a metal-containing terminal oxidase. There are in fact numerous examples in the literature in which plant tissues have responded to such an addition by a greatly reduced O_2 uptake (Table XVI). Disturbing to the concept that a metal-containing terminal oxidase is all-important is the finding that a variety of plant tissues, particularly older parts, do not so respond, and in fact their respiration may be distinctly stimulated by the cyanide addition (Table XVI). The progressively lower inhibitions observed in series of aging organs should be especially noted.

Until the recent demonstration of the (cyanide-insensitive) autoxidation of cytochrome b_7 in the aroid spadix (p. 110), it had been customary to assign this CN-resistant component to a flavoprotein oxidase (van Herk, 1937; James and Beevers, 1950). Alternatively, of course, particularly when a low con-

TABLE XVI

EFFECTS OF CYANIDE AND AZIDE ON O_2 UPTAKE OF PLANT TISSUES

MATERIAL	CN'		N$_3$'		AUTHORS
	Conc. (M)	O_2 Uptake (% of Control)	Conc. (M)	O_2 Uptake (% of Control)	
Fresh potato discs	0.001	29	—	—	Thimann et al., 1954
Washed potato discs	0.001	84	—	—	Thimann et al., 1954
Pea internodes	0.0001	11	—	—	Eichenberger and Thimann, 1957
Carrot slices	0.001	20–30	0.001	24	Marsh and Goddard, 1939
Young carrot leaves	0.001	33	0.001	43	Marsh and Goddard, 1939
Old carrot leaves	0.001	100–150	0.001	100–107	Marsh and Goddard, 1939
"		—	0.001 (pH 5.2)	63	Stenlid, 1949
"		—	0.01 (pH 5.2)	19	Stenlid, 1949
Wheat embryos	0.001	9	0.001	26	Brown and Goddard, 1941
Various pollens	0.0002	14–84	—	—	Okunuki, 1939
6-day barley roots	0.0005	31	0.001	37	James and Boulter, 1955
"		—	0.001 (pH 4.4)	0	Stenlid, 1949
Wheat roots, 0–2 mm.	0.0005	30	0.001	42	Eliasson and Mathieson, 1956
Wheat roots, 2–5 mm.	0.0005	33	0.001	55	Eliasson and Mathieson, 1956
Wheat roots, 5–10 mm.	0.0005	39	0.001	64	Eliasson and Mathieson, 1956
Wheat roots, 30–40 mm.	0.0005	46	0.001	78	Eliasson and Mathieson, 1956
Wheat roots, 10–15 mm.	—	—	0.001 (pH 4.4)	0	Stenlid, 1949
Atropa leaves (increasing age)	0.002	35	0.001	38	MacDonald and de-Kock, 1958
	0.002	41	0.001	46	MacDonald and de-Kock, 1958
	0.002	60	0.001	74	MacDonald and de-Kock, 1958
	0.002	74	0.001	81	MacDonald and de-Kock, 1958
	0.002	112	0.001	92	MacDonald and de-Kock, 1958
	0.002	116	0.001	106	MacDonald and de-Kock, 1958

Table XVI—*Continued*

MATERIAL	CN'		N₃'		AUTHORS
	Conc. (M)	O₂ Uptake (% of Control)	Conc. (M)	O₂ Uptake (% of Control)	
Skunk-cabbage flowers	0.001	96–123	—	—	Hackett, 1957
Philodendron flowers	0.001	128	—	—	Yocum and Hackett, 1957
Arum spadix	0.001	100–150	—	—	James and Beevers, 1950
					Hackett and Simon, 1954
					Bendall, 1958
Mycorrhizal roots of beech	0.001	140–160	0.004	250	Harley *et al.*, 1956

trol rate of respiration is encountered, the lack of inhibition might be ascribed to a relative excess of a CN-sensitive oxidase, so that even when the inhibitor was present sufficient activity remained to account for the O_2 uptake observed. A further possibility has been raised by the demonstration of an autoxidizable cytochrome, b_3, in microsomes (Martin and Morton, 1956; Hackett, 1956). The actual function of this component is in some doubt, and the amounts present are certainly not adequate to account for the high rates of cyanide-resistant respiration occasionally encountered.

Negative results with other inhibitors of metal enzymes are likewise subject to several different interpretations. Again, when less than 100% inhibition is obtained, the question is whether a metal-containing oxidase has been incompletely inactivated or whether a part of the electron transfer occurs through some other pathway. Curves relating concentration of inhibitor to response are valuable, though frequently they are not provided.

The results with cyanide and azide are thus seen to be equivocal; the resistant fraction of O_2 uptake may represent an incompletely inhibited metal-containing oxidase, a flavin oxidase, or an induced bypass (autoxidizable cytochrome b_7?) around cyanide-sensitive stages. Even in those tissues where sizable inhibitions are obtained, additional evidence is needed to decide whether the cytochrome or some other system is operating.

Diethyldithiocarbamate (DIECA) has been widely used by James (1953) with a view to differentiating between iron- and copper-containing oxidases *in vivo*. However, even in the extracted systems the affinity for the two metals is not sufficiently different to allow complete inhibition of one system without affecting the other, and the range in which any differentiation is possible is narrow. The instability of DIECA makes it a far from ideal inhibitor, but by its use it has been established that the O_2 uptake of older barley root tips is qualitatively different from that of wheat, for example. The greater sensitivity to DIECA in older barley roots is one of the reasons for supposing that ascorbic oxidase is important in their respiration (James, 1953; James and Ward, 1957). We may note, however, that Honda (1957) has shown that it is still possible even after DIECA treatment to extract sufficient ascorbic oxidase and cytochrome oxidase to account for the respiratory O_2 uptake of uninhibited roots.

Sensitivity to carbon monoxide. The light-reversible inhibition by CO is a diagnostic test for the participation of cytochrome oxidase (Table XVII). The inhibition depends on the relative amounts of CO and O_2 present (Warburg, 1927) and only becomes appreciable at high levels of CO. In most of the experiments with this inhibitor, the material is exposed to a gas mixture containing CO and O_2 in 9:1 or 19:1 ratio, and the O_2 uptake is compared with that in similar mixtures of N_2 and O_2. The use of higher levels of CO must be preceded by a demonstration that respiratory O_2 uptake is not curtailed by the correspondingly low O_2 level. For if it is so curtailed, the operation of an oxidase with low affinity for O_2 might be discriminated against. Higher effective levels of CO (without lowering the O_2 tension to critical levels) may be achieved by a procedure due to Schneiderman and Wil-

TABLE XVII

EFFECTS OF CARBON MONOXIDE ON O_2 UPTAKE OF PLANT TISSUES

Material	Pro- por- tion CO O_2	% of Control Rate	Light-Reversal	Authors
Lupine seedlings	3.2/1	62–81	Complete	Tang, 1932
Unwashed potato discs	19/1	44	+	Schade et al., 1949
Unwashed potato discs	19/1	41	Complete	Thimann et al., 1954
Various pollens	19/1	34–81	Complete	Okunuki, 1939
Pea internodes	5/1	40	Complete	Eichenberger and Thi- mann, 1947
Beech roots	19/1	65	+	Harley and ap Rees, 1959
Barley embryos	19/1	43	+	James and Boulter, 1955
5-day barley root tips	19/1	93	–	James and Boulter, 1955
Older barley root tips	19/1	100	–	James and Boulter, 1955
5-day barley leaf	19/1	54	+	Daly and Brown, 1954
Pine needles	10/1	40	–	Kempner, 1936
Carrot slices	19/1	34	+	Marsh and Goddard, 1939
Young carrot leaves	19/1	62	+	Marsh and Goddard, 1939
Old carrot leaves	19/1	105–110	–	Marsh and Goddard, 1939
Various roots (9 spe- cies)	19/1	35–62	+ (Complete)	Webster, 1954
Cucumber fruits	19/1	46	+	Webster, 1954
Apple fruit	19/1	54	None	Webster, 1954
Washed potato discs	19/1	100–125	–	Thimann et al., 1949
Washed potato discs	19/1	93	–	Schade et al., 1949
Wild-plum leaf	19/1	119–129	None	Daly, 1954
Beech mycorrhizal roots	19/1	126	None	Harley and ap Rees, 1959
Skunk-cabbage flower	19/1	115–174	–	Yocum and Hackett, 1957
Philodendron flower	19/1	126–141		Yocum and Hackett, 1957

liams (1954), in which the tissue is exposed to CO-O_2 mixtures under several atmospheres pressure.

A variety of tissues have yielded clear evidence in experiments with CO that cytochrome oxidase is the important terminal agent in respiration. Table XVII lists a selection of results, and in several tissues the inhibition which develops is that expected at the prevailing O_2 tension if cytochrome oxidase were catalyzing the whole of the O_2 uptake (Warburg, 1927). It is, moreover, considerably or entirely removed by light. The possibility remains that incomplete reversal is due to inadequate light penetration into bulky tissues; but in the apple tissue, which was the only completely refractory one in Webster's group, this possibility was apparently disposed of (but see p. 103). As in the cyanide experiments, the youngest tissues (embryos) are the most strongly inhibited; many of the older tissues are resistant, and in some CO actually stimulates O_2 uptake. Table XVII includes data from leaves and barley roots in which such a progression from young to old tissues is shown (see also Ducet and Rosenberg, 1957).

By a very effective use of the mass spectrometer, Daly and Brown (1954) were able to show that in green leaves, too, light may bring about a considerable reversal of CO inhibition of respiration (Figure 13). When the light was turned on, of course an O_2 output from photosynthesis began; but the effects on O_2 uptake were easily followed in spite of this by recording changes in mass 34. Earlier experiments by Kempner (1936) and by Ducet and Rosenberg (1952) demonstrated the light-reversible inhibition of leaf respiration by using leaves which were prevented from carrying out photosynthesis by a mild chloroform treatment.

A very interesting tissue in its response to CO is the potato tuber. When freshly cut, discs are strikingly inhibited by CO, and light reverses this inhibition. The discs are at this time very sensitive to cyanide as well. When the tissues are aerated at 25° C for 12 hours, the control rate of respiration is more than doubled. However, with the development of this extra respiration, the sensitivity to CO (and cyanide) diminishes drastically, and the respiration may indeed be

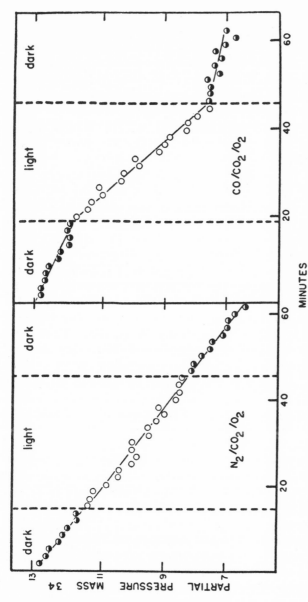

FIGURE 13.—CO inhibition of barley-leaf respiration and its photoreversibility. The open circles show the progress of O_2 uptake in the light, and the half-closed circles O_2 uptake in the dark. ($N_2/CO_2/O_2$ 93:5:2 and $CO/CO_2/$ O_2 93:5:2). Note that O_2 uptake is measured by following changes in Mass 34 in the gas phase which is enriched with heavy oxygen. (Daly and Brown, 1954.) (Courtesy Archives Biochem. Biophys.)

stimulated by CO after a period of washing. Thimann *et al.* (1954) conclude from their results with CO and ancillary experiments that in the aged discs a cytochrome system insensitive to CO and HCN or a flavoprotein with high O_2 affinity must be operating. MacDonald (1959) has recently provided extensive data on the profound changes in sensitivity to inhibitors during washing of various storage tissues.

However, although the rate of O_2 uptake in such discs is not inhibited by CO and 0.001 M KCN, the growth (water uptake) remains, nevertheless, sensitive to these inhibitors, and the CO inhibition of these metabolic processes is, additionally, reversed by light. (Analogous effects of HCN and azide on salt accumulation by beech mycorrhizas by Harley's group [Harley *et al.*, 1956] will be recalled.) It is clear then that important energy-requiring events in the cells of the aerated discs remain dependent on cytochrome oxidase—as indeed they are in a variety of tissues studied by the Harvard school. The conclusion thus seems inevitable that cytochrome oxidase is operating in the washed discs and that, when CO is added, it is inhibited according to the rules. The fact that the rate of O_2 uptake is not slowed down must then be ascribed to the diversion of electrons normally passing through the cytochrome c-a-a_3 sequence to some other outlet to O_2— a facultative outlet which is resistant to CO and HCN and yet with a relatively high affinity for O_2. An autoxidizable cytochrome b_7 component (p. 110) would provide just such a shunt. Besides suggesting a basis for the CO resistance of washed potato discs (and perhaps that of other tissues), the invoking of cytochrome b_7 would account rather readily for the observation that CO might actually stimulate respiration (Table XVII). Thus, if the cytochrome c-a-a_3 steps are blocked, the accompanying phosphorylations will also be prevented, and traffic through b_7 would lead to much lower overall phosphorylations (Hackett and Haas, 1958a). The results would be a shift in the intracellular adenylates in favor of ADP, a consequent stimulation of glycolysis (p. 149), and a lowering of the Pasteur effect (cf. Daly, 1954).

It is implied from the foregoing (since CO inhibitions,

when they are obtained, are more or less reversed by light) that cytochrome oxidase rather than phenol oxidase is operating. A neat separation of effects on the two systems was observed by Nakabayashi (1954), working with apple tissue. He showed that the browning reaction of fruit extracts was due to phenol oxidase, and this could be inhibited by CO and not reversed by light. The CO inhibition of the O_2 uptake of fruit, on the other hand, was reversed by light. He concluded that browning and respiration were not connected, in spite of the tremendous activity of the phenol oxidase present. We may note that apple tissue was the only one of twelve tested by Webster (1952) in which light failed to relieve CO inhibition; possibly in his material a major part of the O_2 uptake observed was not respiratory but was due to phenol oxidase action in injured cells. Middleton (1955) also made a clear distinction between the ability of beet and potato discs to oxidize substrates for phenol oxidase and the participation of this enzyme in the respiration, and Hatch et al. (1959) ruled out the participation of phenol oxidase in apple fruit by use of the inhibitor phenylthiourea.

Effects of O_2 tension on respiratory rates. It is clear from Table XVIII that the various terminal oxidases have quite different affinities for O_2. The extracted cytochrome oxidase has a particularly high affinity, while ascorbic oxidase and flavoproteins are not saturated with substrate (O_2) even at 1 atmosphere. On the assumption that the affinity of the terminal oxidase will be reflected in the form of the curve relating O_2 tension to rate of respiratory O_2 consumption, some authors (e.g., Bonner, 1957) have put considerable stress on such curves as criteria by which the participation of individual oxidases might be judged.

However, as Hartree (1957), Mapson (1958), and others have pointed out, the O_2 saturation curve is an unequivocal criterion only if it is known that the terminal oxidase step is the rate-limiting one throughout the range of O_2 concentrations used. Thus an apparently high affinity for O_2 might result in a tissue in which an enzyme such as ascorbic acid oxidase, with low O_2 affinity, was active and present in excess,

TABLE XVIII

EFFECTS OF O_2 TENSION ON O_2 UPTAKE BY PLANT TISSUES

Material	O_2 Level at Which O_2 Uptake Was 50% of That in Air	Authors
Sugar cane	ca. 4%	Bielski, 1958
Skunk-cabbage spadix	ca. 4%	Hackett, 1957
Philodendron flower	0.2%	Yocum and Hackett, 1957
Potato	0.5%	Thimann et al., 1954
Pea internodes	3%	Eichenberger and Thimann, 1957
Rice seedlings	2.7%	Vlamis and Davis, 1943
Barley seedlings	2.7%	Vlamis and Davis, 1943
Carrot discs	2.5%	Marsh and Goddard, 1939
Various pollens	2.5%	Okunuki, 1939
Avocado fruit	ca. 4%	Biale, 1956
Lemon fruit	ca. 7%	Biale and Young, 1947
Beech mycorrhizas	6%	Harley et al., 1956
Spinach leaves	1%	Platenius, 1943
Asparagus shoots	1%	Platenius, 1943
Snap beans	1%	Platenius, 1943
Shelled peas	5%	Platenius, 1943
Mango fruits	6.5%	Singh et al., 1937

if the respiratory rate at O_2 tensions greater than 2% was being governed by the pace of preceding reactions in the chain. Again, a misleadingly low O_2 affinity would be observed in a tissue in which the terminal oxidase was cytochrome oxidase but in which penetration of O_2 to the respiratory centers was restricted.

Goddard's (1948) statement that there are few data on the effect of O_2 tension on the respiratory rate where the diffusion factor can be eliminated still stands. There are no experiments with higher plant tissues such as those of Winzler (1941) on yeast in which the O_2 relationships were shown to be determined by the speed of reaction of O_2 with the oxidase and in which diffusion was experimentally ruled out as a contributory factor.

These considerations should be borne in mind in making deductions from the data on O_2 effects in Table XVIII. It is significant in view of the above that some of the lowest values for higher plant tissues have been observed when precautions were taken which diminished the contribution of O_2 diffusion through several layers of cells or through a water barrier. Those tissues whose respiration is increased at O_2 levels greater than those in air are the bulkiest ones. It does not therefore seem necessary at present to invoke the general participation of oxidases with low O_2 affinity in the respiration of plant tissues.

Addition of substrates for terminal oxidases. The rationale behind experiments of this sort is that if a particular oxidase is the important one in respiration, the O_2 uptake of the tissue concerned will be increased by adding its substrate. Clearly one can deduce nothing about the *functional* oxidase from such experiments. Indeed, the much more modest conclusion that a particular oxidase is *present* cannot always be drawn from evidence of the ability of its substrate to stimulate O_2 uptake by the tissue, because for catechol and ascorbate, for example, several oxidation mechanisms other than their specific oxidases may be present. Nevertheless, the rapid O_2 uptake, unaccompanied by an equivalent CO_2 output, which occurs when ascorbate is added to barley roots (Butt and Hallaway, 1958) or catechol to potato discs (Boswell and Whiting, 1938) can be reasonably ascribed to ascorbic oxidase and phenol oxidase, respectively. This of course is a far cry from showing that the substrate is acting in a cyclic fashion and by so doing is bringing about an accelerated breakdown of the natural respiratory substrate (Middleton, 1955).

It should be clear from the foregoing sections that, so far as positive evidence goes, the results point unmistakably to the central importance of the cytochrome system in plant respiration. Those who feel that cytochrome oxidase is not important in particular tissues use as evidence the failure to detect the enzyme, the lack of inhibition by cyanide, and the failure of CO inhibition or its reversal by light. So long as reasonable explanations of these experimental difficulties are possible, the temptation is to regard the cytochrome system as the major agent by which electrons are transferred to O_2.

The case for the participation of catechol oxidase rests primarily on the occasionally incomplete reversal of CO inhibition by light and the action of selective but not completely specific inhibitors. Serious claims for a major participation of catechol oxidase have been made in the past, for example in the respiration of potato tubers (Boswell and Whiting, 1938) and spinach leaves (Bonner and Wildman, 1946). Newer evidence has shown that the cytochrome system is present and, from the CO evidence, also functioning in such tissues. Some of the Russian workers, particularly Mikhlin and Kolesnikov (1947) and Pshenova (1956), have advanced claims, on what appears to be incomplete evidence, for the participation of phenol oxidases in the respiration of leaves.

James's group has made a sustained argument for the participation of ascorbic oxidase in barley-root respiration (James, 1953; James and Boulter, 1955; James and Ward, 1957). However, the case now rests almost entirely on the diethyldithiocarbamate evidence, since it is now clear that the cytochrome system is present (Fritz and Beevers, 1955a; Honda, 1955b; Lubell and Bonner, 1958; and James and Boulter, 1955) and at least to some degree functional (James and Lundegårdh, 1959) in roots which previously were thought to be without this equipment. Mapson and Moustafa (1956) have suggested, from measurements of ascorbate reducing and oxidizing capacities, the distribution of the enzyme, and inhibitor data, that the ascorbate system may account for 20–25% of the respiratory O_2 uptake of germinating pea cotyledons. The fluctuations in dehydroascorbate level in response to aerobic and anaerobic conditions described by Barker and Mapson (1952) and Mapson (1958) will be recalled. Marrè's group attaches some importance to the ascorbate system. They demonstrated that dehydroascorbate has striking inhibitory effects on some dehydrogenases and suggest that the ascorbate-glutathione system may play a regulatory role by affecting other electron-transferring systems in plant respiration (Marrè and Arrigoni, 1955; Marrè and Laudi, 1956).

The proponents of peroxidase are not numerous, although the recent emphasis on its oxidative functions (p. 80) earns it further consideration. Lundegårdh (1954, 1955) considers from spectrophotometric evidence that peroxidase may be of some importance in yeast respiration and possibly to a minor extent in wheat roots, and Mikhlin and Kolesnikov (1947) consider that it may participate in the respiration of barley leaves.

Any consideration of the respiratory participation of glycolic oxidase, the only cyanide-resistant agent in Table XV, must be confined to a possible role in leaf respiration. Although explanations for CN insensitivity other than the participation of a nonmetal-containing oxidase are currently popular, the active cyanide-stable oxidation of hexose phosphates by nonparticulate extracts from pea leaves must be borne in mind. A direct test for the participation of glycolic oxidase in leaf respiration has recently been proposed by Zelitch (1958). He used bisulfite compounds to inhibit the enzyme *in vivo*, without inhibiting the glyoxylic reductase. In light, but not in darkness, amounts of glycolate accumulated in tobacco leaves which were almost equivalent to the expected O_2 uptake. He suggested that the O_2 uptake in light must therefore be ascribed to glycolic oxidase. It would certainly be of value to have this interesting proposal confirmed by mass spectrometric evidence that O_2 uptake in the light is stopped by the inhibitors, since there are serious implications for the light reversal of CO inhibition of leaf respiration (p. 101).

Thus, in spite of the current and justified tide of opinion against the view that soluble oxidases have important roles in respiration, it would not be wise at present to read them out of the picture entirely. A fractional or temporary participation in particular tissues must remain a possibility. Certainly, if there is any contact between reduced nucleotides generated in the nonparticulate phase of the protoplasm and the various soluble reductases and oxidases, it would seem highly unlikely that the nucleotides would survive a journey to the mitochondria.

The strict association of the cytochrome oxidase with the mitochondria is of course a very potent argument in favor of its having a major role in plant respiration. Certainly, insofar as succinate oxidation is a partial reaction in this process, the cytochrome system must be involved. Since the mitochondria are also the site of the generation of the great bulk of reduced nucleotides and the cytochrome system has been demonstrated to play a role in their oxidation, its participation must be a major one. A final consideration is that the oxidations occurring under the influence of the cytochrome system in the mitochondria result in the generation of ATP. At the present time, in spite of efforts to extend the list, the cytochrome system stands alone among the oxidase systems as one from whose action ATP can be generated.

THE RESPIRATION OF AROID SPADICES; CYANIDE-RESISTANT RESPIRATION

Van Herk's (1937) extensive work on the tropical *Sauramatum* and more recently that of James and Beevers (1950) on a variety of more accessible aroid spadices has focused attention on the unusual respiration of these tissues. The respiration is remarkable, first of all, by its very magnitude—values as high as 20,000 μl O_2/hr. g f. wt. have recently been observed in the opening flowers of *Arum maculatum* (Simon, 1959). Secondly, the addition of classical inhibitors of cytochrome oxidase (cyanide, azide, and CO) does not slow down the O_2 uptake; indeed, some quite appreciable stimulations have been observed (Tables XVI and XVII).

Now, although resistance to cyanide is far from unique in plant tissues, as the data in Table XVI indicate, it is certainly unusual to find a resistant respiration of such high activity. Investigations on the cyanide-stable respiration of these tissues might reasonably be expected to offer clues on the nature of this type of respiration wherever it occurs. In fact, a series of publications in the past few years from British and American laboratories has brought to light valuable new information on this problem. At the present time the aroid spadix is one of the few plant tissues on which extensive and definitive work has been done at all levels of investigation.

James and Beevers (1950), on the basis of a variety of experiments with whole *Arum* spadix tissues and aqueous extracts, which also take up O_2 vigorously, were led to ascribe the cyanide insensitivity to the operation of some flavoprotein oxidase. One of the reasons for this suggestion was the fact that the rate of O_2 uptake was dependent on O_2 tension from 0–100% O_2. It has since become clear from the work of Yocum and Hackett (1957) on *Philodendron* and *Peltandra*, Hackett (1957) on *Symplocarpus*, and Simon (1957) on the English *Arum* that the conclusion from this experiment was invalid. The rate of O_2 diffusion through the water layer was inadequate to support the respiration of this highly active material. When experiments were carried out with thin sections in a moist atmosphere, an entirely different picture of the O_2 relationship was obtained. The respiration was saturated with O_2 at very low partial pressure; in fact the $pO_2(50)$ is one of the lowest recorded for plant tissues (Table XVIII), though few have been investigated with due regard to the diffusion limitations. These findings make it extremely unlikely that an autoxidizable flavin could be the terminal oxidase.

In fact there have now been successful isolations from aroid tissues of highly active mitochondria containing cytochrome oxidase (e.g., Hackett and Simon, 1954; Bonner and Yocum, 1956; Bendall and Hill, 1956; Simon, 1957; Hackett, 1957) whose O_2 uptake may furthermore be tightly coupled to phosphorylation (Hackett and Haas, 1958a). The O_2 uptake of such preparations with certain substrates is relatively resistant to cyanide, though by no means so strikingly as that of the intact tissues (e.g., Hackett and Simon, 1954; James and Elliott, 1955). The rate of O_2 uptake by the mitochondria is considerably less than that of a corresponding weight of intact parent tissue; but this is a usual finding, and the possibility must be entertained that the cytochrome system in the mitochondria is entirely responsible for the normal O_2 uptake of this tissue (Bendall, 1958). Simon's (1959) recent demonstration that higher assays of cytochrome oxidase are obtained after digitonin treatment is encouraging to such a view.

When slices of *Arum* spadix were made anaerobic in the spectroscope, a very striking absorption spectrum with bands at 605, 560, and 550 mμ became visible (Bendall and Hill, 1956; Bendall, 1958). The intensity of the 560 mμ band (corresponding to the cytochrome "b") was particularly strong—in contrast to the usual situation in plant materials. Similar investigations on other spadix tissue (Yocum and Hackett, 1957; Bonner and Yocum, 1956) made it clear that possession of this strong b band is characteristic of those in which the CN-stable respiration is so vigorous. However, the b component has been shown to be different from previously described cytochromes, and one part of it is referred to as b_7 (Bendall and Hill, 1956). Although the b band is prominent, it is important to emphasize that the bands of cytochromes a and c are themselves quite noticeable, and these components undergo oxidation and reduction in the manner expected if they were functioning in O_2 uptake. In the presence of cyanide these components revert to the reduced condition (Hackett, 1959). In striking contrast is the behavior of b_7, which remains largely in the oxidized condition on the addition of cyanide in air but which is reduced in anaerobic conditions. This feature seems to fit this component for a key role in cyanide-stable respiration.

More extensive spectrophotometric experiments with mitochondria isolated from the spadix tissues seem to bear out this possibility. The b_7 component, like the other cytochromes, is attached to the particles, and difference spectra have indicated clearly the functioning of cytochromes a and c and the unusual behavior of b_7 in response to cyanide (Figure 14). The cytochrome oxidase activity of the mitochondria was strongly inhibited by 10^{-4} M cyanide and, as expected, cytochromes a and c were strongly reduced (Bendall, 1958). The oxidation of malate and citrate (Simon, 1957) and succinate (Bendall, 1958) were only partially inhibited by an amount

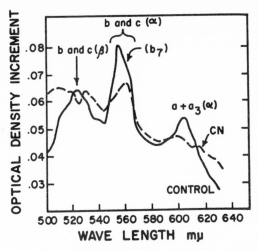

FIGURE 14.—Cytochromes in an aroid flower. The effect of cyanide (0.001 M) on the difference spectrum of a mitochondrial preparation from *Symplocarpus*. Note the relatively small effect of cyanide on the b_7 region (after Hackett and Haas, 1958).

of cyanide sufficient to wipe out cytochrome oxidase activity. A further important finding by Hackett and Haas (1958a) was that cyanide induced a very significant fall in P/O ratio (see Chapter 5) when organic acids were being oxidized (Table XIX). The participation of the usual cytochromes b and c in these mitochondrial oxidations (in the absence of cyanide) was indicated by their sensitivity to antimycin A and urethane, which inhibit electron transfer between these two components. By equilibrating with systems of known redox potential, Bendall and Hill (1956) have shown that the E_0' of cytochrome b_7 is lower than that of the usual cytochrome b and that its behavior in urethane was also different.

The most obvious and attractive explanation, which is supported by the above evidence and which has been suggested by several of the authors, is the following. A cyanide-insensitive pathway represented by the autoxidizable b_7 is present which may transport electrons in the uninhibited tissue but which is perforce of primary importance when transport

TABLE XIX

EFFECTS OF DNP, AZIDE, AND CYANIDE ON OXIDATIVE PHOSPHORYLATION
BY *Symplocarpus* MITOCHONDRIA; SUBSTRATE: α-KETOGLUTARATE (HACK-
ETT AND HAAS, 1958)

	O_2 Uptake (μ atoms)	iP Esterified (μ moles)	P/O
Control	9.3	21.0	2.2
10^{-5} M DNP	7.4	3.8	0.5
Control	5.6	14.5	2.6
10^{-3} M Azide	3.9	7.4	1.9
Control	1.7	6.1	3.4
4.6×10^{-4} M Cyanide	2.2	3.4	1.6

through the conventional system is prevented by cyanide.
The following considerations make it unlikely that traffic
through b_7 to O_2 occurs normally in the mitochondria and,
by implication, in the intact tissue:

a. The very high P/O ratios (close to the theoretical value
of 4) obtained when mitochondria were oxidizing α-
ketoglutarate (Hackett and Haas, 1958a) would seem to
require participation of b and c and cytochrome oxidase
for their achievement.

b. The effect of cyanide on the P/O ratio suggests that
in its presence two phosphorylative steps have been
prevented, which would result if electrons were funneled through the $b_7 \rightarrow O_2$ sequence in a nonphospho-
rylating bypass (Table XIX).

c. Although the mechanism of action is quite different
from that of DNP, the effect of cyanide would thus be
a sort of "uncoupling," as Hackett and Haas point out.
We might reasonably infer that as a result of the consequent increase in ADP supply (Chapter 7) the over-all
respiratory rate might actually be stimulated by cyanide, which in fact it frequently is.

The second possibility which had been recognized as an alternative by the above authors has been given greater promi-

nence in a recent paper by Chance and Hackett (1959). In this paper powerful techniques of Chance (1957) were brought to bear, and the results represent the most thorough analysis of the problem to date. The simultaneous recordings of O_2 uptake (polarographically detected) and of the parallel changes in oxidation of the DPN and the cytochromes in response to experimentally imposed variables have provided extremely valuable data. From measurements on the rates of changes of oxidation state on adding inhibitors and substrates, these authors conclude that b_7 is on the pathway of electron transfer from substrate to the oxidase in the untreated tissue. They emphasize that although the cytochromes a and c are strongly reduced in the presence of azide or cyanide they are never *completely* reduced. Chance had shown previously that electron transfer can occur at an undiminished rate even though the steady-state condition of individual components might be altered, provided that their concentration is nonlimiting—the so-called "cushioning" effect. In view of this, Chance and Hackett feel that even in the inhibited system electron transfer may still be occurring actively through the cytochrome c system. They state as one of their conclusions from their extensive work that "it is premature to give serious consideration to alternative pathways for electron transfer" so long as this possibility remains open.

It may, however, be seriously questioned whether the cytochrome oxidase is in fact nonlimiting, particularly under conditions where its activity is strongly reduced by cyanide or azide. The measurements which have been attempted on cytochrome oxidase in these tissues (Simon, 1959) are certainly not encouraging to the view that something of the order of a tenfold excess of cytochrome oxidase is present— which presumably would be required to account for the phenomenal O_2 uptake of CN-treated material. In addition there seems to be no ready explanation on the "excess cytochrome oxidase" hypothesis for the fact that cyanide may induce sizable *stimulations* of O_2 uptake and at the same time reduce the P/O ratio (which are neatly accounted for on the bypass hypothesis). Finally we may note that the effects of

HOQNO (2-alkyl-4-hydroxyquinoline-N-oxide) on b_7 oxidation observed by Chance and Hackett are ascribed to an action between b and c, although it seems quite likely that it actually interferes with the autoxidation of b_7 (Lightbown and Jackson, 1956).

For a final settlement of these questions it would clearly be of value to have more information on the properties of cytochrome b_7 itself. The present definition of the autoxidation of b_7 does not rule out the operation of an additional (noncytochrome) component between b_7 and O_2, but the system must have a high O_2 affinity for it to be functionally significant (Yocum and Hackett, 1957).

The relevance of the investigations on aroid respiration to cyanide resistance in other materials should be clear. Although it is not suggested that there is only one explanation of resistance to cyanide (see p. 107), the bypass hypothesis seems to be the most attractive, since it offers a reasonable explanation for the stimulations of respiration by CN, CO, and azide and the concurrent reductions in the ability of the tissue to do useful work.

REFERENCES

ARNON, D. I. Plant Physiol. 24, 1 (1949).
AKAZAWA, T., and CONN, E. E. Jour. Biol. Chem. 232, 403 (1958).
ANDERSON, D. G., STAFFORD, H. A., CONN, E. E., and VENNESLAND, B. Plant Physiol. 27, 675 (1952).
BARKER, J., and MAPSON, L. W. New Phytol. 51, 90 (1952).
BARKER, J., and MAPSON, L. W. New Phytol. 58, 58 (1959).
BEEVERS, H. Plant Physiol. 29, 265 (1954).
BEEVERS, H., and JAMES, W. O. Biochem. Jour. 43, 636 (1948).
BENDALL, D. S. Biochem. Jour. 70, 381 (1958).
BENDALL, D. S., and HILL, R. New Phytol. 55, 206 (1956).
BERTRAND, G. Compt. rend. 120, 266 (1895).
BHAGVAT, K., and HILL, R. New Phytol. 50, 112 (1951).
BIALE, J. B. Am. Jour. Botany 33, 363 (1956).
BIALE, J. B., and YOUNG, R. E. Am. Jour. Botany 34, 301 (1947).
BIALE, J. B., YOUNG, R. E., POPPER, C. S., and APPLEMAN, W. E. Physiol. Plant. 10, 48 (1957).
BIELSKI, R. L. Australian Jour. Biol. Sci. 11, 315 (1958).
BONNER, J., and WILDMAN, S. G. Arch. Biochem. Biophys. 10, 497 (1946).
BONNER, W. D. Plant Physiol. 30, xx (1955).
BONNER, W. D. Plant Physiol. 31, xli (1956).
BONNER, W. D. Ann. Rev. Plant Physiol. 8, 427 (1957).

BONNER, W. D., and YOCUM, C. S. Plant Physiol. **31,** xli (1956).
BOSWELL, J. G., and WHITING, G. C. Ann. Botany (N.S.) **2,** 845 (1938).
BROWN, A. H., and GODDARD, D. R. Am. Jour. Botany **28,** 319 (1941).
BUTT, V. S., and HALLAWAY, M. Biochem. Jour. **69,** 20P (1958).
CHANCE, B., in *The Enzymes* (J. B. SUMNER and K. MYRBACK, eds.), Academic Press, New York (1951).
CHANCE, B., in *Methods in Enzymology* (S. P. COLOWICK and N. KAPLAN, eds.), Academic Press, New York (1957).
CHANCE, B., and HACKETT, D. P. Plant Physiol. **34,** 33 (1959).
CHOW, C. T., and BIALE, J. B. Physiol. Plant. **10,** 64 (1957).
CLAGGETT, C. O., TOLBERT, N. E., and BURRIS, R. H. Jour. Biol. Chem. **178,** 977 (1949).
CLAYTON, R. A. Arch. Biochem. Biophys. **81,** 404 (1959).
CONN, E. E., KRAEMER, L. M., LIU, PEI-NAN, and VENNESLAND, B. Jour. Biol. Chem. **194,** 1943 (1952).
CONN, E. E., and SEKI, S. L. Fed. Proc. **16,** 167 (1957).
CONN, E. E., and VENNESLAND, B. Jour. Biol. Chem. **192,** 17 (1951).
CRANE, F. L. Plant Physiol. **32,** 619 (1957).
CRANE, F. L. Plant Physiol. **34,** 128 (1959).
DALY, J. M. Arch. Biochem. Biophys. **51,** 24 (1954).
DALY, J. M., and BROWN, A. H. Arch. Biochem. Biophys. **52,** 380 (1954).
DAWSON, C. R., and TARPLEY, W. B., in *The Enzymes* (J. B. SUMNER and K. MYRBACK, eds.), Academic Press, New York (1951).
DUCET, G., and ROSENBERG, A. J. Compt. rend. **234,** 549 (1952).
EICHENBERGER, E., and THIMANN, K. V. Arch. Biochem. Biophys. **67,** 466 (1957).
ELIASSON, L., and MATHIESEN, I. Physiol. Plant. **9,** 265 (1956).
FRANKE, W., SCHULZ, I., and DEBOER, W. Z. Phys. Chem. **303,** 70 (1956).
FRANKENBURG, W. G. Adv. in Enzymol. **10,** 325 (1950).
FREUDENBERG, K. Chem. Ber. **89,** 92 (1959).
FRITZ, G., and BEEVERS, H. Plant Physiol. **30,** 309 (1955a).
FRITZ, G., and BEEVERS, H. Arch. Biochem. Biophys. **55,** 436 (1955b).
FRITZ, G., MILLER, W. G., BURRIS, R. H., and ANDERSON, L. Plant Physiol. **33,** 159 (1958).
FRIGERIO, N. A., and HARBURY, H. A. Jour. Biol. Chem. **231,** 135 (1958).
FUJIMURA, K., and IKEDA, S. Mem. Res. Inst. Food Sci. Kyoto Univ. **13,** 45 (1957).
GIBBS, M. Plant Physiol. **29,** 34 (1954).
GODDARD, D. R. Am. Jour. Botany **31,** 270 (1944).
GODDARD, D. R., and MEEUSE, B. J. D., Ann. Rev. Plant Physiol. **1,** 207 (1950).
GODDARD, D. R., and STAFFORD, H. A. Ann. Rev. Plant Physiol. **5,** 115 (1954).
GOODWIN, B. C., and WAYGOOD, E. R. Nature **174,** 517 (1958).
HACKETT, D. P. Int. Rev. Cytol. **4,** 143 (1955).
HACKETT, D. P. Plant Physiol. **31,** 111 (1956).
HACKETT, D. P. Jour. Exp. Botany **8,** 157 (1957).
HACKETT, D. P. Plant Physiol. **33,** 8 (1958).
HACKETT, D. P. Ann. Rev. Plant Physiol. **10,** 113 (1959).
HACKETT, D. P., and HAAS, D. W. Plant Physiol. **33,** 27 (1958a).
HACKETT, D. P., and HAAS, D. W. Plant Physiol. **33,** vii (1958b).
HACKETT, D. P., and SCHNEIDERMAN, H. A. Arch. Biochem. Biophys. **47,** 190 (1953).
HACKETT, D. P., SCHNEIDERMAN, H. A., and THIMANN, K. V. Arch. Biochem. Biophys. **47,** 205 (1953).

116   HARRY BEEVERS

HACKETT, D. P., and SIMON, E. W. Nature 173, 162 (1954).
HANSL, N. R. Osterr. Akad. Wiss. Math. Naturw. Sitzber. Abt. 164, 25 (1955).
HARLEY, J. L., and AP REES, T. New Phytol. 58, 364 (1959).
HARLEY, J. L., McCREADY, C. C., BRIERLEY, J. K., and JENNINGS, D. H. New Phytol. 55, 1 (1956).
HARTREE, E. F. Adv. in Enzymol. 18, 1 (1957).
HATCH, M. D., PEARSON, J. A., MILLERD, A., and ROBERTSON, R. N. Australian Jour. Biol. Sci. 12, 167 (1959).
HASKINS, F. A. Plant Physiol. 30, 74 (1955).
HESS, E. H. Arch. Biochem. Biophys. 74, 198 (1958).
HIGUCHI, T. Physiol. Plant. 10, 356 (1957).
HIGUCHI, T. J. Biochem. (Tokyo) 45, 515 (1958).
HILL, R., and HARTREE, E. F. Ann. Rev. Plant Physiol. 4, 115 (1953).
HONDA, S. Plant Physiol. 30, 174 (1955a).
HONDA, S. Plant Physiol. 30, 402 (1955b).
HONDA, S. Plant Physiol. 32, 23 (1957).
HOLMAN, R. T., and BERGSTROM, S., in The Enzymes (J. G. SUMNER and K. MYRBACK, eds.), Academic Press, New York (1951).
HOWARD, F. D., and YAMAGUCHI, Y. Plant Physiol. 32, 418 (1957).
HUMPHREYS, T. E. Plant Physiol. 30, 46 (1955).
HUMPHREYS, T. E., and CONN, E. E. Arch. Biochem. Biophys. 60, 226 (1956).
JAMES, W. O. Biol. Revs. 28, 245 (1953).
JAMES, W. O., and BEEVERS, H. New Phytol. 49, 353 (1950).
JAMES, W. O., and BOULTER, D. New Phytol. 54, 1 (1955).
JAMES, W. O., and CRAGG, J. M. New Phytol. 42, 28 (1943).
JAMES, W. O., and ELLIOTT, D. C. Nature 175, 89 (1955).
JAMES, W. O., HEARD, C. R. C., and JAMES, G. M. New Phytol. 43, 62 (1944).
JAMES, W. O., and LUNDEGÅRDH, H. Proc. Roy. Soc. B150, 7 (1959).
JAMES, W. O., ROBERTS, E. A. H., BEEVERS, H., and DEKOCK, P. C. Biochem. Jour. 43, 626 (1948).
JAMES, W. O., and WARD, M. Proc. Roy. Soc. B147, 309 (1957).
JENSEN, W. A. Plant Physiol. 30, 426 (1955).
JOHNSON, G., and SCHAAL. L. A. Am. Potato Jour. 34, 200 (1957).
KEILIN, D. Proc. Roy. Soc. B98, 312 (1925).
KEILIN, D., and HARTREE, E. F. Proc. Roy. Soc. B119, 141 (1936).
KEMPNER, W. Plant Physiol. 11, 605 (1936).
KENTEN, R. H. Biochem. Jour. 55, 350 (1953).
KENTEN, R. H. Biochem. Jour. 59, 110 (1955).
KENTEN, R. H., and MANN, P. J. G. Biochem. Jour. 52, 125 (1952a).
KENTEN, R. H., and MANN, P. J. G. Biochem. Jour. 52, 130 (1952b).
KENTEN, R. H., and MANN, P. J. G. Biochem. Jour. 53, 498 (1953).
KOLESNIKOV, P. A. Uspeckhi Soviemennoi Biol. 38, 133 (1954).
KOLESNIKOV, P. A. Doklady. Akad. Nauk S.S.S.R. 112, 909 (1957).
KOLESNIKOV, P. A., and EMENOVA, S. V. Doklady Akad. Nauk. S.S.S.R. 109, 152 (1956).
KUBOWITZ, F. Biochem. Zeitschr. 293, 308 (1937).
LAUDI, G. Atti accad. nazl. lincei rend., classe sci., fis. mat. e nat. 19, 164 (1955).
LIEBERMAN, M. Science 127, 189 (1958).
LIGHTBOWN, J. W., and JACKSON, F. L. Biochem. Jour. 63, 130 (1956).
LUBELL, A. R., and BONNER, W. D. Plant Physiol. 33, vi (1958).
LUNDEGÅRDH, H. Nature 171, 520 (1953).
LUNDEGÅRDH, H. Ark. f. Kemi 7, 451 (1954).

LUNDEGÅRDH, H. Physiol. Plant. 8, 84 (1955a).
LUNDEGÅRDH, H. Biochem. Biophys. Acta 20, 469 (1956).
LUNDEGÅRDH, H. Biochem. Biophys. Acta 27, 355 (1958).
LUNDEGÅRDH, H. Biochem. Biophys. Acta 35, 340 (1959).
MACDONALD, I. Ann. Botany (N.S.) 23, 241 (1959).
MACDONALD, I. R., and DEKOCK, P. C. Physiol. Plant. 11, 464 (1958).
MACLACHLAN, G. A., and WAYGOOD, E. R. Can. J. Biochem. Physiol. 34, 905 (1956).
MACMUNN, C. A. Phil. Trans. Roy. Soc. 177, 267 (1885).
MAHLER, H. Ann. Rev. Biochem. 26, 17 (1957).
MANN, P. J. G. Biochem. Jour. 50, 360 (1952).
MANN, P. J. G. Biochem. Jour. 59, 609 (1955).
MAPSON, L. W. Ann. Rev. Plant Physiol. 9, 119 (1958).
MAPSON, L. W., and GODDARD, D. R. Biochem. Jour. 49, 592 (1951).
MAPSON, L. W., and MOUSTAFA, E. M. Biochem. Jour. 62, 248 (1956).
MARRÈ, E., and ARRIGONI, O. Atti accad. nazl. lincei rend., classe sci., fis. mat. e nat. 19, 460 (1955).
MARRÈ, E., and LAUDI, G. Atti accad. nazl. lincei rend., classe sci., fis. mat. e nat. 20, 806 (1956).
MARRÈ, E., and LAUDI, G. Atti accad. nazl. lincei rend., classe sci., fis. mat. e nat. 23, 287 (1957).
MARRÈ, E., and SERVATTEZ, O. Atti accad. nazl. lincei rend., classe sci., fis. mat. e nat. 5, 208 (1956).
MARSH, P. B., and GODDARD, D. R. Am. Jour. Botany 26, 767 (1939).
MARTIN, E. M., and MORTON, R. K. Nature, 176, 1113 (1955).
MARTIN, E. M., and MORTON, R. K. Biochem. Jour. 62, 696 (1956).
MARTIN, E. M., and MORTON, R. K. Biochem. Jour. 65, 404 (1957).
MASON, H. S. Adv. in Enzymol. 4, 99 (1955).
MASSEY, V. Biochem. Biophys. Acta 37, 314 (1960).
MATTHEWS, M. B. Jour. Biol. Chem. 189, 695 (1951).
MIDDLETON, L. J. Jour. Exp. Botany 6, 422 (1955).
MIKHLIN, D. M., and KOLESNIKOV, P. A. Biokhimiya 12, 452 (1947).
MILLER, G. W., EVANS, H. J., and SISLER, E. Plant Physiol. 33, 124 (1958).
MILLERD, A., BONNER, J., AXELROD, B., and BANDURSKI, R. S. Proc. Nat. Acad. Sci. 37, 855 (1951).
MOTHES, K., and WAGNER, A. N. Biokhimiya 22, 171 (1957).
NASON, A., WOSILAIT, W. D., and TERRELL, A. J. Arch. Biochem. Biophys. 48, 233 (1954).
NAKABAYASHI, T. Nippon Nogei-Kagaku-Kaishi 28, 212 (1954).
NEWCOMB, E. H. Proc. Soc. Exp. Biol. Med. 76, 504 (1951).
NOLL, C. R., and BURRIS, R. H. Plant Physiol. 29, 261 (1954).
ONSLOW, M. W. Principles of Plant Biochemistry, Cambridge Univ. Press (1931).
OKUNUKI, K. Acta Phytochimica 11, 27 (1939).
PLATENIUS, H. Plant Physiol. 18, 671 (1943).
POWERS, W. H., LEWIS, S., and DAWSON, C. L. Jour. Gen. Physiol. 27, 167 (1944).
PSHENOVA, K. V. Biokhimiya 21, 279 (1956).
ROBERTS, E. A. H., and WOOD, D. J. Biochem. Jour. 49, 414 (1951).
ROMANO, A. H., and NICKERSON, W. J. Jour. Biol. Chem. 208, 409 (1956).
SCHADE, A. L., LEVY, H., BERGMAN, L., and HARRIS, S. Arch. Biochem. Biophy 20, 211 (1949).
SCHNEIDERMAN, H. A., and WILLIAMS, C. M. Biol. Bull. 106, 210 (1954).

SIEGEL, S. M. Physiol. Plant. 6, 134 (1953).
SIEGELMAN, H. W. Arch. Biochem. Biophys. 56, 97 (1955).
SIMON, E. W. Jour. Exp. Botany 8, 20 (1957).
SIMON, E. W. Biochem. Jour. 69, 67 (1958).
SIMON, E. W. Jour. Exp. Botany 10, 125 (1959).
SINGH, B. N., SESHAGIRI, P. V. V., and GUPTA, S. S. Ann. Botany (N.S.) 1, 311 (1937).
SISLER, E. C., and EVANS, H. J. Plant Physiol. 33, 255 (1958).
SISLER, E. C., and EVANS, H. J. Plant Physiol. 34, 81 (1959).
SLATER, E. C. Adv. in Enzymol. 20, 147 (1958).
SMILLIE, R. M. Australian Jour. Sci. 17, 217 (1955a).
SMILLIE, R. M. Australian Jour. Biol. Sci. 8, 2 (1955b).
SMITH, L., and CHANCE, B. Ann. Rev. Plant Physiol. 9, 449 (1958).
STENLID, G. Physiol. Plant. 2, 61 (1949).
STERN, H., and JOHNSTON, F. B. Plant Physiol. 32, 476 (1957).
STOUT, M. J. Am. Soc. Sugar Beet Technol. 8, 404 (1954).
STUMPF, P. K. Jour. Biol. Chem. 223, 643 (1956).
STUTZ, R. E. Plant Physiol. 32, 31 (1957).
SUZUKI, Y. Naturwiss. 44, 514 (1957).
SZENT-GYÖRGYI, A. Jour. Biol. Chem. 90, 383 (1931).
TAGAWA, K., SHIN, M., and OKUNUKI, K. Nature 183, 111 (1959).
TANG, P. S. Jour. Gen. Physiol. 15, 655 (1932).
TEWFIK, S., and STUMPF, P. K. Jour. Biol. Chem. 192, 523 (1951).
THEORELL, H., in The Enzymes (J. B. SUMNER and K. MYRBACK, eds.), Academic Press, New York (1951).
THIMANN, K. V., YOCUM, C. S., and HACKETT, D. P. Arch. Biochem. Biophys. 53, 239 (1954).
TOLBERT, N. E., and BURRIS, R. H. Jour. Biol. Chem. 186, 791 (1950).
TOLBERT, N. E., CLAGGETT, C. O., and BURRIS, R. H. Jour. Biol. Chem. 181, 905 (1949).
VAN HERK, A. W. H. Rec. Trav. Bot. Neerland. 34, 69 (1937).
VARTAPETYAN, B. B., and KURSANOV, A. L. Doklady Akad. Nauk. S.S.S.R. 104, 272 (1955).
VLAMIS, J., and DAVIS, A. R. Plant Physiol. 18, 685 (1943).
WARBURG, O. Biochem. Zeitschr. 189, 354 (1927).
WAYGOOD, E. R. Can. J. Research (C)28, 7 (1950).
WAYGOOD, E. R., and MACLACHLAN, G. A. Physiol. Plant. 9, 607 (1956).
WAYGOOD, E. R., OAKS, A., and MACLACHLAN, G. A. Can. J. Botany 34, 891 (1956).
WEBSTER, G. C. Am. Jour. Botany 39, 739 (1952).
WEBSTER, G. C. Plant Physiol. 29, 399 (1954).
WINZLER, R. J. Jour. Cell. Comp. Physiol. 17, 263 (1941).
WOSILAIT, W. D., NASON, A., and TERRELL, A. J. Jour. Biol. Chem. 206, 272 (1954).
YAMADA, N., and OOTA, Y. Kagaku 28, 91 (1958).
YOCUM, C. S., and HACKETT, D. P. Plant Physiol. 32, 186 (1957).
ZELITCH, I. Jour. Biol. Chem. 201, 719 (1953).
ZELITCH, I. Jour. Biol. Chem. 216, 553 (1955).
ZELITCH, I. Jour. Biol. Chem. 224, 251 (1957).
ZELITCH, I. Jour. Biol. Chem. 233, 1299 (1958).
ZELITCH, I., and OCHOA, S. Jour. Biol. Chem. 201, 707 (1953).

Chapter 5

The Energetics of Respiration

The common feature of the various oxidative steps of the EMP and pentose phosphate sequences and of the TCA cycle which have been outlined in earlier chapters is the transfer of pairs of electrons, particularly to pyridine nucleotides. In the breakdown of 1 mole of glucose by these reactions, we can point to the origin of 10 moles of PNH, which, when oxidized to H_2O by appropriate means, would account for 5 of the 6 moles of O_2 absorbed. The reducing equivalents transferred directly to the cytochrome system by succinic dehydrogenase account for the sixth mole of O_2 absorbed (Table XX).

Now, since the oxidation of 1 mole of PNH to H_2O and PN results in a release of some 52,000 cals., the total PNH production during the respiration of 1 mole of glucose represents some 520,000 cals., or 77% of the 674,000 cals. of free energy available. To this 77% must be added the energy represented by (a) the ATP generated in glycolysis (20,000 cals./mole glucose), (b) the cytochrome b (Fe^{++}) produced in succinate oxidation (some 70,000 cals./mole glucose) and (c) the thioester bond in succinyl-CoA (20,000 cals./mole glucose). It thus becomes clear that some 90% of the free energy available is initially conserved in these forms; less than 10% is dissipated as heat in all of the interconversions of the various reaction sequences leading to the formation of PNH and substrate level ATP—a remarkably small loss. The bulk of the free energy of the sugar used in respiration is released in the reoxidation of the nucleotides, and it is in the mechanism of their oxidation that we must look for the generation of something more useful than heat—in a word, for the "payoff" reactions of respiration.

We should perhaps distinguish here between the fate of

TABLE XX

REDUCING EQUIVALENTS GENERATED DURING GLUCOSE OXIDATION

Oxidative Step	Reduced Product	Moles/ Mole Glucose	Equiva- lent O_2 Absorp- tion
1. Glucose-6-P → 6-P-Gluconate	TPNH	1	$\frac{1}{2}$
2. 6-P-Gluconate → Pentose-P + CO_2	TPNH	1	$\frac{1}{2}$
3. Phosphoglyceraldehyde → Phos- phoglyceric acid	DPNH (TPNH)	2	1
4. Pyruvate → Acetyl-CoA	DPNH	2	1
5. Isocitrate → α-Ketoglutarate	DPNH (TPNH)	2	1
6. α-Ketoglutarate → Succinyl-CoA	DPNH	2	1
7. Malate → Oxalacetate	DPNH	2	1
8. Succinate → Fumarate	Cyt. b (Fe^{++})	2	1

PNH generated in reactions outside the mitochondria (Reactions 1–3 in Table XX) and that resulting from reactions of the TCA cycle. It now appears that intramitochondrial PNH is oxidized through the built-in cytochrome system but that in the best mitochondrial preparations this pathway may not be directly available to PNH produced on the outside. We should note that PNH, wherever it is generated, might be utilized in synthetic or reductive events and thus represent the link between endergonic reactions and the exergonic reactions of respiration. Thus considerable quantities of PNH are consumed in nitrate and sulphate reduction, fat synthesis from acetyl units, hexose production from 3-C precursors, and in glutamate and alcohol synthesis. It is conceivable that when such reductive events are occurring it is the extramitochondrial PNH (generated in the EMP and pentose phosphate sequences) which is primarily used. To the extent that such utilization does occur, the R.Q. will be increased, and such changes are indeed observed (Chapters 9 and 12).

It is, of course, conceivable that reducing equivalents generated by soluble enzymes could be introduced into the mitochondria through the agency of a reducible compound and its soluble dehydrogenase. If this reduced compound (e.g., isocitrate, malate, lactate, α-glycerophosphate) were then re-oxidized in the mitochondria, the net effect would be equivalent to a transport of the PNH. However, although the machinery is present, there is no experimental evidence for the operation of this device in living plant cells.

A third possibility, which cannot be excluded, is that extra-mitochondrial PNH is subject to oxidation by the various soluble electron-transfer and oxidase systems. If such a fate does befall that fraction of the nucleotides reduced outside the mitochondria, it would, on our present understanding, result in a further loss of free energy as heat, since it has not as yet been possible to demonstrate any formation of ATP during these oxidations. This may in fact be the major fate in mature tissues where glucose utilization by the pentose phosphate pathway is extensive and synthetic reductive events are presumably at a minimum.

Although it seems that different plant tissues and particles may show their own peculiarities of behavior, the evidence is now good that the oxidation of DPNH in mitochondria follows the general pathway DPNH → flavoprotein → cytochrome b → cytochrome c → cytochrome a + a_3 → O_2 and that of succinate leads to a junction in this sequence at cytochrome b (Table XIV). In considering what the useful product of this stepwise electron transfer might be, we should note the changes in free energy which result (Figure 15). If we take the ∆H of hydrolysis of the terminal phosphate of ATP as 10,000 cals., it will be seen that at each of the steps involved an amount of energy is released which could conceivably account for the synthesis of one mole of ATP from ADP and iP. The demonstration that such a synthesis of ATP did in fact occur during the oxidation of mitochondrial DPNH represented an important milestone in the development of biochemical knowledge. It has been clear for several years that, under the best conditions, the efficiency of this coupling in mitochondria from liver is that predicted if, in fact, the synthesis of one mole of ATP did accompany each stage of oxidation shown in Figure 15. The values for moles

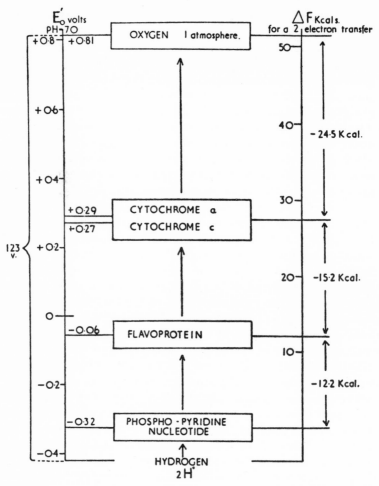

FIGURE 15.—Oxidation reduction potentials of intermediates and free-energy changes involved in the transfer of two hydrogen electrons from DPNH to oxygen. (Street, 1950.)

ATP synthesized from ADP and iP per mole intramitochondrial DPNH oxidized approach 3. Some 60% of the energy released during DPNH oxidation may thus be converted into ATP.

This coupling of oxidation to phosphorylation can be measured by determining the O_2 uptake and concomitant incorporation of iP into ATP when a TCA-cycle intermediate is being oxidized by mitochondria. Usually hexokinase and glucose are added as a trap for ~P; the ADP is thereby regenerated, and the disappearance of iP (which is trapped as glucose-6-phosphate) is used as a measure of ATP synthesis. The P/O value (micromoles iP esterified/microatoms oxygen absorbed) reflects the efficiency with which the energy lost in electron transfer is conserved. α-Ketoglutarate is the substrate most frequently used in such studies, and the best P/O ratios are close to 4 (1 substrate level phosphorylation results from the succinyl-CoA and 3 result from DPNH oxidation). Values close to those expected if the nucleotides were channeled through a similar sequence have been obtained for other TCA-cycle acids (Table XXIV). It should be noted that when substrate amounts of the acids are added, the electron-transfer sequence may be largely pre-empted by the initial oxidative step but the oxidation may proceed further. In order to restrict the oxidation of α-ketoglutarate to one step, malonate is frequently added (Table XXIV).

It should not be thought from the foregoing that an efficiently coupled ATP synthesis is the inevitable accompaniment of O_2 uptake when mitochondria oxidize TCA-cycle acids. On the contrary, the apparatus for O_2 uptake, fragile though it is, is yet considerably more robust than that gearing it to phosphorylation. Thus various maltreatments of the mitochondria during extraction, aging, and exposure to a variety of chemical agents (p. 126) result in a relatively great loss of phosphorylating ability with a consequent lowering of the P/O value. Values close to theoretical ones are obtained only in the most carefully prepared particles; the P/O value is frequently taken as the criterion by which the intactness and general well-being of the mitochondria are judged. It is usually assumed that mitochondria which yield the highest P/O values are the least altered from their condition in the living cell.

A most important property of "tightly coupled" mitochondria is that they show a definite requirement for ADP and iP, as would be expected if these were reactants as indicated in Figure 22. When ADP is added to such mitochondria well supplied with substrate, O_2 uptake is strikingly increased and thus ATP synthesis must be obligatorily linked to electron transfer. It is this obligatory coupling which at once makes the system so highly efficient and, what is even more important, allows a very precise regulation of the rate of ATP synthesis by the rate of its consumption (see p. 149). For since the total amount of adenylate available to the mitochondria is fixed, the supply of ADP becomes limiting as it is converted to ATP, and, unless the terminal ~P of ATP is utilized or split off hydrolytically, the rate of O_2 uptake will fall. ATP utilization (e.g., in the production of glucose-6-P), by replenishing the ADP supply, allows the electron transfer to proceed, and ATP synthesis is thereby restored.

At the present time, in spite of intensive effort from many different groups, the precise mechanism whereby ATP synthesis is achieved during electron transfer is not known. Most of the informed speculation centers around high-energy compounds which have a transient existence during the oxidations (Table XXI). A corresponding mystery surrounds the mode of action of compounds such as 2,4-dinitrophenol (DNP)

TABLE XXI

Skeleton Outline of Oxidative Phosphorylation during Electron Transfer* (Lehninger, 1959)

Carrier (red) + X + oxidant → Carrier (Ox) ~ X + reductant
Carrier (Ox) ~ X + iP → Carrrier (Ox) + P ~ X
P ~ X + ADP → ATP + X

Over all: Carrier (red) + ADP + iP + oxidant →
                    Reductant + ATP + carrier (Ox)

---

* The present information on the location of phosphorylation sites indicates that a series of events as suggested above occurs when DPNH, cytochrome b (Fe^{++}), and cytochrome a (Fe^{++}) are the reduced carriers, and the succeeding members of the sequence (flavin [Ox], cytochrome c [Fe^{+++}], and cytochrome a$_3$ [Fe^{+++}]) are the oxidants which become reduced. X is presumed to be an accessory enzyme.

which have the important and interesting property of destroying the coupling between oxidation and phosphorylation and are thus known as "uncoupling agents." The present indications are that DNP induces the breakdown of a transitory ~P compound (Table XXI) and thus at once renders the sequence independent of ADP supply and prevents the production of ATP. These compounds had been known to interfere drastically with growth and other endergonic reactions in cells and at the same to induce stimulations in O_2 uptake (Chapter 7).

The recognition that the esterification of iP by mitochondria was prevented by DNP and that the rate of O_2 uptake, normally limited by ADP supply, was actually increased under the appropriate conditions (p. 148) implicated the mitochondria as the sites of ATP production in the cell and offered an adequate explanation of the observed effects *in vivo*.

ATP PRODUCTION IN PLANT MITOCHONDRIA

Although none of the pioneering work on ATP synthesis was done with mitochondria from plants, it has since been shown that, in particulate preparations from a wide variety of plant tissues, oxidation of acids of the TCA cycle is accompanied by an efficient incorporation of iP into ATP. Thus P/O values reasonably close to the theoretical ones have now been obtained for a variety of mitochondria during the oxidation of α-ketoglutarate, succinate, and citrate (Table XXIV). Requirements for Mg^{++} and adenylate and the beneficial effect of adding fluoride to inhibit adenosine triphosphatase activity have been demonstrated (Tables XXII and XXIII). In addition, some success in demonstrating phosphorylation associated with single stages in electron transport has been obtained. Thus Fritz and Naylor (1956) working with mung-bean mitochondria were able to demonstrate that some esterification accompanied the oxidation of reduced cytochrome c and also that ATP formation occurred when the cytochrome c–cytochrome oxidase was bypassed by providing ferricyanide as the electron acceptor during oxidation

TABLE XXII

COFACTOR REQUIREMENTS FOR OXIDATIVE PHOSPHORYLATION BY
LUPINE MITOCHONDRIA (CONN AND YOUNG, 1957)

Conditions	O_2 uptake (μ atoms)	iP Esterified (μ moles)	P/O
Complete system*	5.2	12.9	2.5
minus AMP	0.6	0	0
minus $MgSO_4$	4.4	5.7	1.3

* α-Ketoglutarate, 0.02 M; AMP (or ADP), 1.5×10^{-3} M; DPN, 10^{-4} M; $MgSO_4$, 1.5×10^{-3} M; malonate, 0.01 M; glucose, 0.01 M; NaF, 0.01 M; sucrose, 0.4 M; plus mitochondria in 3-ml. buffer.

TABLE XXIII

THE EFFECTS OF NaF, HEXOKINASE, AND DNP ON OXIDATIVE PHOSPHORYLATION IN CASTOR-BEAN MITOCHONDRIA (AKAZAWA AND BEEVERS, 1957)

Conditions	O_2 Uptake (μ atoms)	iP Esterified (μ moles)	P/O
Complete system*	11.2	24.5	2.2
minus NaF	13.7	21.6	1.6
minus NaF and hexokinase	6.9	5.1	0.7
plus DNP (2×10^{-4} M)	10.0	5.9	0.6
without NaF and hexokinase plus DNP	17.4	0	0

* α-Ketoglutarate, 0.01 M; glucose, 0.05 M; NaF, 0.02 M; ATP, 1 mg; DPN, 1 mg; TPP, 0.5 mg; CoA, 0.1 mg; hexokinase, 1 mg; plus mitochondria in 2-ml buffer.

(Table XXV). Kaufman and Alivisatos (1955) have shown that ATP synthesis is coupled to the conversion of succinyl-CoA (the oxidation product of α-ketoglutarate) to succinate, according to the following equation:

$$\text{Succinyl-S-CoA} + \text{ADP} + \text{iP} \underset{}{\overset{Mg^{++}}{\rightleftharpoons}} \text{Succinate} + \text{HS-CoA} + \text{ATP}$$

The so-called "phosphorylating enzyme" was extensively purified from spinach leaves.

The tightness of coupling of oxidation to phosphorylation in some plant mitochondria has been demonstrated by the re-

TABLE XXIV

OXIDATIVE PHOSPHORYLATION BY MITOCHONDRIA FROM PLANTS

Plant Part (Author)	Substrate	O_2 Uptake (μ atoms)	iP Esterified (μ moles)	P/O
Cauliflower buds (Laties, 1953c)	Succinate	—	—	1.4
	α-Ketoglutarate	—	—	2.4
Pea stems (Smillie, 1955)	Succinate	24.5	35.5	1.5
	α-Ketoglutarate	16.2	50.1	3.1
Pea leaves (Smillie, 1956)	Succinate	25.5	40.4	1.6
	α-Ketoglutarate	14.3	41.8	2.9
	Isocitrate	10.8	29.4	2.8
	Citrate	9.4	23.6	2.5
Sweet potato (Lieberman and Biale, 1956)	α-Ketoglutarate	16.8	36.0	2.2
	α-Ketoglutarate plus malonate	8.9	29.6	3.3
Etiolated lupine seedlings (Conn and Young, 1957)	Succinate	6.7	11.4	1.7
	α-Ketoglutarate	16.2	25.1	1.5
	α-Ketoglutarate plus malonate	6.0	21.9	3.6
Castor-bean seedlings (5 day) (Akazawa and Beevers, 1957)	Succinate	3.5	5.5	1.6
	α-Ketoglutarate	9.5	19.4	2.1
	Citrate	10.4	22.4	2.2
	Malate	11.0	22.0	2.0
Avocado fruit (Biale et al., 1957)	α-Ketoglutarate	8.0	11.6	1.5
	α-Ketoglutarate plus malonate	5.7	11.5	2.0
Cabbage (Freebairn and Remmert, 1957)	α-Ketoglutarate	11.2	42.5	3.8
	Oxalacetate	20.7	45.3	2.2
	Fumarate	18.7	42.8	2.3
	Succinate	10.2	23.6	2.3
Skunk-cabbage spadix (Hackett and Haas, 1958)	α-Ketoglutarate	2.76	10.12	3.7

TABLE XXV

PHOSPHORYLATION LINKED TO SUCCINATE AND ASCORBATE
OXIDATION IN MITOCHONDRIA (FRITZ AND NAYLOR, 1956)

Source of Mitochondria	Substrate	Oxidant	P/O
Mung bean	Succinate	O_2	1.89
Cauliflower	Succinate	O_2	0.92
Mung bean	Ascorbate*	O_2	0.53
Cauliflower	Ascorbate*	O_2	0.12
Mung bean	Succinate†	Ferricyanide	0.19

* Ascorbate was used as a reductant for cytochrome c Fe^{+++}.

† Ferricyanide was used as an oxidant for cytochrome c Fe^{++} (anaerobic experiment).

quirement for ADP or a precursor and by the stimulatory effects of a ~P trapping system or uncoupling agent (see Table XXIII and Laties, 1953a,b). It should be noticed that under the usual conditions of P/O determinations (i.e., in the presence of hexokinase and glucose) the rate of O_2 uptake which is obtained may not be susceptible to further increase by DNP (Table XXIII) although phosphorylation is abolished. In the absence of the ~P trap, i.e., where the rate of O_2 uptake is limited by the rate of ATP turnover, considerable stimulations may be induced by DNP (Table XXIII) or a variety of uncoupling agents (Gaur and Beevers, 1959). Contradictory reports of the effects of uncoupling agents on the O_2 uptake of plant mitochondria capable of giving high P/O ratios can probably be accounted for on this basis. A comparable situation is found *in vivo* (p. 156) where the amount of DNP-stimulated respiration is apparently determined by the rate of ATP turnover existing before the addition of the uncoupling agent.

The available evidence indicates that in plant mitochondria a sequence of phosphorylative events occurs which is similar to that which has been much more intensively studied in mitochondria from liver. When the details of this process are finally elucidated, it seems certain that they will apply equally to the mechanism of ATP synthesis in plant mitochondria. It seems reasonable to suppose that those mitochondria which produce ATP efficiently are in general representative of mitochondria *in vivo*. It is clear that uncoupled or inefficient mitochondria may result from maltreatment or exposure to harmful agents during preparations, but it must also be recognized that changes in the intrinsic activity of the particles may occur naturally during normal growth and aging (see, e.g., Akazawa and Beevers, 1957; Lund *et al.*, 1958).

REFERENCES

Akazawa, T., and Beevers, H. Biochem. Jour. **67,** 115 (1957).

Biale, J. B., Young, R. E., Popper, C. S., and Appleman, W. E. Physiol. Plant. **10,** 48 (1957).

Conn, E. E., and Young, L. C. T. Jour. Biol. Chem. **226,** 23 (1957).

Freebairn, H. T., and Remmert, L. F. Plant Physiol. **32,** 374 (1957).

Fritz, G. G., and Naylor, A. W. Physiol. Plant. **9,** 247 (1956).

Gaur, B. K., and Beevers, H. Plant Physiol. **34,** 427 (1959).

Hackett, D. P., and Haas, D. W. Plant Physiol. **33,** 27 (1958).

Kaufman, S., and Alivisatos, S. G. A. Jour. Biol. Chem. **216,** 141 (1955).

Laties, G. G. Physiol. Plant. **6,** 199 (1953a).

Laties, G. G. Physiol. Plant. **6,** 215 (1953b).

Laties, G. G. Plant Physiol. **28,** 557 (1953c).

Lehninger, A. L. Reviews of Modern Physics **31,** 136 (1959).

Lieberman, M., and Biale, J. B. Plant Physiol. **31,** 420 (1956).

Lund, H. A., Vatter, A. E., and Hanson, J. B. Jour. Biophys. Biochem. Cytol. **4,** 87 (1958).

Smillie, R. M. Australian Jour. Biol. Sci. **8,** 186 (1955).

Smillie, R. M. Australian Jour. Biol. Sci. **9,** 81 (1956).

Street, H. E. Science Progress **38,** 43 (1950).

Chapter 6

Intracellular Localization

of Respiratory Enzymes

Until relatively recently the general procedure in looking for enzymes was to make an aqueous extract of the tissue and to clarify the resulting suspension by centrifuging or chemical treatment. Such clear supernates gave evidence of the existence in plant tissues of a variety of enzymes important in respiration and of many others as well. It has become clear, however, that in concentrating on the soluble phase many of the more interesting enzymes were missed, and it is only in the past fifteen years, when efforts have been directed to the separation of particulate fractions, that the bulk of the respiration mechanism has been elucidated.

The realization that fractions obtained by homogenizing tissues and then centrifuging at graded speeds had different amounts of individual enzymes, and that under carefully controlled conditions some of these fractions were particularly rich in protoplasmic inclusions recognizable to the cytologist, prepared the way for extensive work on the topography of biochemical functions inside the cell. Much of this work, pioneered initially by Bensley and Hoerr (1934) and extended particularly by Schneider and Hogeboom (Hogeboom and Schneider, 1955; Hogeboom *et al.*, 1957; Schneider and Hogeboom, 1956), has been done on mammalian liver. More recently the power of the electron microscope has been brought to bear on these problems, and the identity between purified particulate preparations and the components existing in the cell has been beautifully demonstrated (e.g., by Palade, 1956; Hogeboom *et al.*, 1957; Whaley *et al.*, 1959a).

Ideally, the technique of separating the different cytoplasmic bodies consists of grinding up the tissue in a medium of suitable tonicity at low temperature and in such a way that maximum cell rupture is achieved with a minimum of damage to cellular inclusions. When such a suspension is centrifuged, the densest components—cell-wall fragments and intact cells—settle first, followed in turn by nuclei, chloroplasts, mitochondria, and microsomes as the gravitational field is increased from 50 to 50,000 $\times$ G. In practice, however, no such clear-cut separation is possible. Even if no damage occurs to the particles during grinding, the various classes of particles are not sufficiently different in size and density to allow their complete separation in this way. In an individual cell there are at any given time a range of sizes of some of the components, and among the heterogeneous collection making up the tissue the variety will be extreme. Thus each "fraction" is to some extent contaminated with others, and subsequent washing and resuspension (with inevitable losses of material) and perhaps centrifuging in a density gradient may be necessary to achieve reasonable purity of, say, chloroplasts, nuclei, or mitochondria (Jagendorf, 1955; Kmetec and Newcomb, 1956; James and Das, 1957). Even after such a separation, formidable problems remain in deciding where or whether individual enzymes are truly localized in the particles obtained. Artifacts such as leakage of enzymes from particulate bodies and adsorption of truly soluble enzymes onto particles or interphases are some of the hazards. As Hogeboom and Schneider (1955) have pointed out in a very worth-while article, a convincing case for localization must include valid enzyme assays on the total homogenate as well as on each of the separate fractions, and a satisfactory balance sheet should be provided. Crane (1957) has carefully examined the distribution of some enzyme activities in cauliflower homogenates in this way (Table XXVI), and Martin and Morton (1956a) have provided comparable information from silver beet (Table XXVII). We can deduce that Crane's "Medium" fraction is the richest in mito-

TABLE XXVI

RECOVERY OF ENZYMATIC ACTIVITY IN THE PARTICULATE FRACTIONS
FROM CAULIFLOWER-BUD* HOMOGENATE (CRANE, 1957)

FRACTION	PROTEIN MG.	DPNH-OXIDASE	DPNH-CYT. C REDUCTASE		DPNH-DIAPHORASE	CYTOCHROME OXIDASE
			−ANTIMYCIN	+ANTIMYCIN		
Original homogenate	4,560	128.0	45.0	45.0	129.0	320
Cell debris	69	0.2	0.1	—	1.1	1
Fibers (2,000 × G, 3 min.)	56	63.4	0.8	1.3	3.2	2
Medium (5,000 × G, 10 min.)	307	42.2	12.3	7.7	48.0	77
Medium light (25,000 × G, 10 min.)	124	7.8	4.9	3.7	12.7	9
Packed light (105,000 × G, 15 min.)	112	3.7	3.9	5.6	9.1	4
Fluffy light (105,000 × G, 60 min.)	81	1.2	4.1	4.4	4.2	1
Supernatant solution	3,460	49.0	10.4	10.4	21.0	7
Recovery	4,189	107.5	36.5	33.1	99.3	101

* 540 g wet weight of cauliflower buds.

NOTE: Figures in table are for total activity of enzymes in individual fractions.

TABLE XXVII

DISTRIBUTION OF NITROGEN AND ENZYMATIC ACTIVITIES AMONG FRACTIONS
FROM BEET-PETIOLE DISPERSION (MARTIN AND MORTON, 1956a)

Fraction	Nitrogen	Succinic Dehydrogenase	DPNH-Cytochrome c Reductase	DPNH Diaphorase
Whole dispersion	100	100	100	100
1,500 × G, 15 min.) (unbroken cells, etc.)	8.1	7.0	17.4	17.6
10,000 × G, 15 min. (mitochondria)	7.8	10.6	32.3	13.6
20,000 × G, 15 min. (mixed particles)	2.4	0	21.1*	3.9
50,000 × G, 90 min. (microsomes)	3.6	0	33.7†	8.8
Supernatant	72.0	0	0	62.0
Total recovered	93	18	105	106

* Antimycin-sensitive.

† Antimycin-resistant.

chondria and that, from both tissues, this contains the bulk of the cytochrome oxidase system. However the total recovery of this enzyme from each tissue was incomplete. From the localization of the antimycin-resistant DPNH–cytochrome c reductase and from the force needed to sediment it we can infer that the "Packed light" and "Fluffy light" fractions of Crane corresponded to the microsomes of Martin and Morton. The large protein component of the soluble fraction and its considerable DPNH oxidase activity should also be noted.

Such balance sheets have only rarely been provided in work with plant material; in most biochemical experiments the primary aim, up to the present at least, has been to get a fraction with activity rather than a fraction uncontaminated with other cellular components. In their valuable article, Goddard and Stafford (1954) list some thirty enzymes shown to be located at least in part on particulate structures in plants. More recently, an encouraging number of fairly pure preparations of mitochondria (Crane, 1957; Kmetec and Newcomb, 1956), chloroplasts (Jagendorf, 1955; James and Das, 1957), nuclei (Sissakian et al., 1957b; Stern and Mirsky, 1952; Johnston et al., 1957), and microsomes (Martin and Morton, 1955, 1956a,b,c; T'so et al., 1956) have been isolated.

Smillie (1956a,b,c) has made separations of particulates from green and etiolated pea leaves. The data in Table XXVIII show the distribution of some enzyme activities and of various other constituents among the fractions obtained from green pea leaves. All of the fractions contained some chlorophyll, but by microscopic examination and chemical and enzyme assays it was established that a gross separation of nuclei, plastids, mitochondria, and microsomes had been achieved. We may note the major confinement of DNA to the earliest fraction (nuclei) and a considerable spread in the distribution of RNA. The succinoxidase and cytochrome oxidase were confined to the mitochondrial fraction, and a high level of DPNH–cytochrome c reductase (presumably antimycin A resistant) was present in fraction 6, which still contained small particles (microsomes). It should be noted that no account was taken here of losses during separation,

TABLE XXVIII

Chemical and Enzymatic Properties of Fractions from Green Pea Leaves (Smillie, 1956c)

Fraction	Rel. Centrif. Force, G	X Minutes	Major Components*	Starch % of Total	Protein % of Total	DNA, μg DNA-P/mg N	RNA, μg RNA-P mg N	Chlorophyll, mg/mg N	Succinic Dehydrogenase (Arbitrary Units)	Succinoxidase μ Atoms O/mg N	iP Esterified, μM/mg N	Cytochrome Oxidase (Arbitrary Units)	DPNH-Cytochrome c Reductase
1	35	15	N.	89	7	32	20	0.2	0	0	0	0	0
2	300	15	N.C.C.F.	9	37	8	40	0.76	2	2	3	20	30
3	1,200	15	C.C.F.P.	2	20	7	26	0.73	11	5	8	130	45
4	2,700	30	C.F.P.P.	0	17	3	26	0.59	28	21	33	350	205
5	6,700	15	P.P.P.	0	11	1	28	0.52	18	11	18	240	215
6	17,000	45	—	0	8	2	33	0.42	4	0	1	18	340

* N. = whole nuclei; C. = chloroplasts; C.F. = chloroplast fragments; P. = particles 0.5μ–2μ.

as was done in the experiments shown in Tables XXVI and XXVII. Sufficient definitive work has been done to justify the view that the activities of the plant cell must depend on the interplay between enzymes specifically associated with cyto-plasmic inclusions and those of the nonparticulate or soluble cytoplasm. We have here in fact a concrete realization of what Blackman referred to in the 1920's as "organization resist-ance."

A truly soluble enzyme would be one which was recovered quantitatively in the supernatant solution from a homogenate in which no breakage or leakage from particles had occurred during preparation. Many of the enzymes concerned with respiration have been judged—perhaps prematurely—to be soluble on less rigorous grounds than these, i.e., after ex-traction under conditions where leakage from particles could not be ruled out. There are now in fact strong indications that all enzymes can be obtained in a soluble condition and that their linkage together in the framework of a structural unit containing lipid and other materials represents merely the achievement of efficiency and order out of an otherwise haphazard system depending entirely on chance molecular collisions at each sequential step. Some enzymes are readily removed from their association. Thus mitochondria are surrounded by a differentially permeable membrane, and when this is broken by exposure to a hypotonic solution, as in making an aqueous extract of the tissue, some enzymes, for example the hydrolases and malic and isocitric dehydrogenases, then appear as nonsedimenting ("soluble") components, whereas others, for example the cytochrome oxidase, remain firmly attached to the insoluble residue. Smaller particulate units have in fact been derived from mitochondria by a variety of treatments (Green, 1956) and carry out reactions of terminal electron transfer. These electron-transport particles (E.T.P.) are believed to represent fragments of the cristae or involutions of the mitochondrial wall. Some progress has been made in releasing enzymes in a soluble form from such association. We may note that when acetone powders of whole tissues or derived particles are prepared and then extracted with water, many enzymes that were originally bound quite firmly to cytoplasmic particles can then be found in the soluble fraction.

The various inclusions will now be dealt with in turn and examples provided of the localization of respiratory enzymes. It should be noted that many authors have preferred not to claim any homology with cytologically identifiable components for their fractions but rather identify them either by a statement of the force which was required to sediment them or by a term describing their appearance after sedimenting (Crane, 1957). Others, encouraged by the instances in which fractions separating at 10,000–15,000 × G have been found to be especially rich in identifiable mitochondria (see Hackett, 1955, 1959) which show the staining behavior familiar to the cytologist, and finding that their particles, prepared in a similar manner, have the same enzymatic abilities, have termed such fractions "mitochondrial." The term has thus come to be an operational one for biochemists, but its use in this way has been debated (see Hackett, 1959; Goddard and Stafford, 1954).

The association of the enzymes of the TCA cycle and the

electron-transport system to O_2 with the mitochondrial fraction has now been established for a remarkable variety of plant tissues. However, all of these enzymes are not exclusively confined to the mitochondria, since soluble counterparts exist. It is the fact that the cytochrome system is restricted to the mitochondria (Tables XXVI and XXVIII) that has focused attention on the capacity of these bodies to oxidize various acids; dehydrogenases for particular acids—malic and isocitric, for example—may be equally concentrated elsewhere in the cell (Davies, 1954; Brummond and Burris, 1954). Even for cytochrome oxidase there are reports of anomalous behavior. For example, Sissakian (1958) finds it on chloroplasts and nuclei, while in the best preparations of Jagendorf (1955) and James and Das (1957) it was apparently missing. Whether the failure of many authors (e.g., Stafford, 1951; McClendon, 1953; Webster, 1952; Fritz and Beevers, 1955) to detect this key enzyme in fractions other than mitochondria is due, as Sissakian suggests, to the production of toxic quinones remains to be established. At present, in the face of the very numerous reports of its strict localization in the mitochondria, contamination of other fractions by whole or broken mitochondria appears a more likely explanation of occasionally aberrant behavior. We may note, however, that recent claims have been made for a naturally soluble cytochrome oxidase (Rubin and Ladygina, 1956).

A list of enzymes which have been shown to be associated—but not necessarily exclusively so—with mitochondria would include the following, in addition to those of the TCA cycle and the electron-transport system: various transaminases, glutamate, formate, lactate and α-glycerophosphate dehydrogenases, hexokinase, acetate-activating system, fatty acid β-oxidation system, and TPNH-glutathione reductase.

The high concentration of enzymes catalyzing transfers of electrons in the mitochondria explains the localization of the ability to reduce tetrazolium dyes and Janus Green B *in vivo*, and this fact was useful in establishing that fractions isolated from homogenates of plant material at *ca.* 5,000 $\times$ G were rich in mitochondria before electron-microscope pictures established it beyond doubt. The isolated mitochondria are frequently spherical (roughly 1μ in diameter) rather than elongated, as they usually appear in living plant cells. They are subject to swelling and shrinking in response to changes in the tonicity of the medium. The mitochondrion is a fragile body which loses activity even under the most carefully controlled conditions (see Laties, 1953). Small chemical or physical changes can bring about drastic losses in mitochondrial activity, and the fact that the ability to couple the oxidation of TCA-cycle acids with the esterification of ADP to form ATP is so readily lost prompts the belief that this is perhaps the single most delicate part of the enzymatic machinery. Certainly the efficiency with which electron transport to O_2 is geared to ATP production (measured by the P/O ratio) is the criterion by which mitochondrial preparations are judged; the best or tightly coupled mitochondria are those in which P/O values approach the theoretical ones (p. 123).

The respiratory function of the mitochondria now seems firmly established, but it is still not clear precisely what the traffic into and out of these organelles is when they are functioning *in vivo*. There are indications that they may not be so freely permeable as some experiments *in vitro* might indicate; it now appears unlikely, for example, that reduced nucleotides enter the mitochondria in the cell or that certain TCA-cycle intermediates such as citrate can traverse the membranes (Lehninger, 1957). Nevertheless it must be assumed that ATP can be lost from the mitochondria and that crucial intermediates for biosynthesis (e.g., glutamate, acetyl-CoA) are also able to move from the mitochondrial to other pools inside the cell. The interpretation which has been put on the apparent efficiency of photosynthesis at low light intensities (p. 199) would imply that components from the mitochondria are capable of movement into the chloroplasts.

Cells rich in chloroplasts appear to be rather poorly endowed with mitochondria (James and Das, 1957), and although clear separations are possible by means of the density-gradient technique, it is not known what fraction of the resulting mitochondria came from nonchlorophyllous cells.

Successful isolation of highly efficient mitochondria from green leaves was achieved by Smillie (1955) (see p. 127), although it should be noted that this fraction, like all of the others that he separated, was by no means free from chlorophyll. Freebairn and Remmert (1956), who made a survey of many plant tissues, showed that several green leaves, including cabbage, were among the better sources of active mitochondria. The Russian workers (Sissakian et al., 1957a) find that active mitochondrial ("cyclophorase") preparations can be prepared from pea sprouts only when these are grown under rather temperate conditions; in natural summer illumination at 20°–25° little or no TCA-cycle activity was found in the preparations. It seems likely that the isolation is in some way rendered more difficult rather than that the mitochondria are not functioning in the material grown at the higher temperatures. Similar difficulties in the isolation of mitochondria from green lupine leaves were experienced by Brummond and Burris (1954) in earlier work.

Before the mitochondrial (or any other) system can be logically considered as a major respiratory pathway of general importance in plants it must first be established (a) that it is of reasonably wide distribution and (b) that in individual tissues the quantitative capacity of the system is high enough in relation to the respiratory rate *in vivo* to qualify it for consideration. In the past few years reassuring evidence has appeared on both of these points. The list of tissues (see Hackett, 1959) which have yielded active mitochondria is quite impressive and in numbers of species must by now exceed considerably the animal sources which have been tested. Individual tissues may present problems, but these do not appear insuperable (Lieberman, 1958; Hatch et al., 1959). It should not be thought that all tissues yield equally active mitochondria, but in a fair number the amount of some individual enzymes, such as cytochrome oxidase, has been shown to be more than adequate to account for the rate of respiration. Furthermore, the over-all capacity for pyruvate oxidation has also been shown to occur at a sizable fraction of the rate observed *in vivo*. When the hazards in the way of quantitative isolation are considered, the evidence is encouraging to the view that the mitochondrial oxidation of pyruvate affords a major respiratory pathway. From one tissue, the root tips of corn seedlings, the activity of the extracted mitochondria has been shown to be greater than that required to account for all of the respiratory O_2 uptake (Lund *et al.*, 1958).

The microsomes or ribonucleoprotein particles are completely sedimented only at considerably higher speeds (*ca.* 50,000 $\times$ G) than those that suffice for mitochondria. These particles are believed to originate from the electron-dense parts of the endoplasmic reticulum which permeates the "soluble" phase of the protoplasm in some cells but is less clearly defined in others (Lund *et al.*, 1958; Whaley *et al.*, 1959b; Setterfield *et al.*, 1959). Thus they may not have a completely separate existence in the cell. Microsomes have been isolated from a variety of plant materials, and the relatively high concentration of RNA has been well established (Martin and Morton, 1956a,c; Akazawa and Beevers, 1957; T'so *et al.*, 1956). Martin and Morton estimated the size of their particles from silver beet as 30–300 mμ in diameter. At present the emphasis is on these bodies as sites of protein synthesis (Webster, 1959). However, certain enzymes which could conceivably be of importance in respiration appear consistently to be concentrated on the microsomes. Thus, as shown in Tables XXVI, XXVII, and XXVIII, an antimycin-insensitive DPNH–cytochrome c reductase has been shown to be present in microsomes from several plant tissues. The localization of an autoxidizable cytochrome component, b_3, on such particles (Martin and Morton, 1955) offers the possibility of a cyanide-insensitive oxidation of reduced nucleotides, which is at best however of rather limited capacity. The ability of microsomal particles from the peanut to bring about the release of $C^{14}O_2$ from palmitate-1-C^{14} will be recalled (p. 210).

During the past few years, at the same time as the Sissakian (1958) group has been suggesting the plastids as the site of all manner of activities, including fatty acid and protein synthesis as well as the TCA cycle and cytochrome oxidase, others have been at pains to arrive at pure chloroplast preparations and to demonstrate their inability to oxidize TCA-cycle acids and cytochrome c. Arnon (1955) in particular has repeatedly advanced a case for the ability of chloroplast to carry out the complete reactions of photosynthesis unassisted by other cellular components. This would of course imply that, insofar as those enzymes of the glycolytic and pentose phosphate sequences are involved in photosynthesis, the cell must have a duplicate set of such enzymes outside the chloroplasts.

At present, although reasonably pure preparations of plant nuclei have been obtained, there does not seem to be any evidence that they are of importance as part of the respiratory machinery (Johnston *et al.*, 1957). A contrary view of the Russian authors must again be recorded (Sissakian, 1958).

The "wall fraction," which is usually discarded during enzyme preparation, nevertheless contains considerable amounts of protein which presumably arise from the outer protoplasmic layers or intrusions into the wall proper. It is interesting to note that from some experiments with whole cells it seems that ascorbic oxidase is so located (Butt and Hallaway, 1958; Honda, 1955) and that experiments *in vitro* corroborate this finding. Thus the major part of the ascorbic oxidase in barley roots, pea shoots, and tobacco callus is attached quite tightly to components of the wall fraction and resists determined efforts to remove it. It is not clear what, if any, functional value results from the association; the inhibitor evidence points to a role in growth rather than in respiration (Newcomb, 1951). It has also been suggested that enzymes or components which are localized on the surface layer of protoplasm may play a role in the transport of materials into cells (Rothstein, 1954).

The soluble protein fraction remaining after centrifuging for an hour at $50,000 \times G$ is frequently found to contain about 60–70% of the original protein of the homogenate. In addition to inert protein, this fraction comprises enzymes which were freed from the endoplasmic reticulum and other more rigid inclusions during grinding, as well as truly soluble ones. Respiratory enzymes which are largely confined to this fraction include those concerned with glycolysis (EMP sequence) and with the pentose phosphate pathway (Chapter 2). In addition there are soluble electron-transfer systems including dehydrogenases, reductases, and oxidases (Chapter 4) and enzymes concerned with acid synthesis.

At present we can only speculate about the interplay during respiration between the various fractions which a knowledge of their enzymatic makeup would seem to require. At a minimum it would seem that pyruvate production occurs in the soluble phase, that its oxidation requires its entry into the mitochondria, and that useful products, ATP and perhaps TCA-cycle acids and near relatives, might leak back into the soluble phase. If complete efficiency is achieved in the generation of ATP from nucleotides reduced outside the mitochondria, some means of mitochondrial oxidation must at present be invoked. This might occur through the intervention of some substance which is reduced outside the mitochondria and which may be subsequently oxidized inside, with the production of intramitochondrial PNH and thus of ATP. On the other hand, it is difficult to see how PNH generated in the soluble phase entirely escapes attack by the highly potent soluble oxidation systems (p. 107).

There are good indications that the interrelationships between mitochondrial and soluble respiratory components are a great deal more subtle than is suggested above. Thus there is evidence of reciprocal action in the regulation of over-all respiratory rates and in the Pasteur effect (Chapter 7) brought about through changes in levels of ATP and ADP (von Korff, 1959). In green cells there is, in addition, circumstantial evidence for movements of respiratory products from mitochondria to chloroplasts (Chapter 11). At present there are no powerful tools for investigating the implications of this localization of enzymatic function; in vivo the various movements are probably further complicated by active transfer systems localized at protoplasmic and intraprotoplasmic membranes.

REFERENCES

AKAZAWA, T., and BEEVERS, H. Biochem. Jour. 67, 110 (1957).
ARNON, D. I. Science 122, 9 (1955).

BENSLEY, R. R., and HOERR, N. Anat. Rec. 60, 449 (1934).
BRUMMOND, D. O., and BURRIS, R. H. Jour. Biol. Chem. 209, 755 (1954).
BUTT, V. S., and HALLAWAY, M. Biochem. Jour. 69, 20P (1958).
CRANE, F. L. Plant Physiol. 32, 619 (1957).
DAVIES, D. D. Proc. Roy. Soc. B142, 155 (1954).
FREEBAIRN, H. T., and REMMERT, L. F. Plant Physiol. 31, 259 (1956).
FRITZ, G. J., and BEEVERS, H. Plant Physiol. 30, 309 (1955).
GODDARD, D. R., and STAFFORD, H. A. Ann. Rev. Plant Physiol. 5, 155 (1954).
GREEN, D. E., in *Enzymes: Units of Biological Structure and Function* (H. O.
   GAEBLER, ed.), Academic Press, New York (1956).
HACKETT, D. P. Inter. Rev. Cytol. 4, 143 (1955).
HACKETT, D. P. Ann. Rev. Plant Physiol. 10, 113 (1959).
HATCH, M. D., PEARSON, J. A., MILLERD, A., and ROBERTSON, R. N. Australian
   Jour. Biol. Sci. 2, 167 (1959).
HONDA, S. Plant Physiol. 30, 174 (1955).
HOGEBOOM, G. H., and SCHNEIDER, W. C., in *The Nucleic Acids*, Vol. II (E.
   CHARGAFF and R. N. DAVIDSON, eds.), Academic Press, New York (1955).
HOGEBOOM, G. H., KUFF, E. L., and SCHNEIDER, W. C. Inter. Rev. Cytol. 6,
   425 (1957).
JAGENDORF, A. Plant Physiol. 30, 138 (1955).
JAMES, W. O., and DAS, V. S. R. New Phytol. 56, 325 (1957).
JOHNSTON, F. B., NASATIR, M., and STERN, H. Plant Physiol. 32, 124 (1957).
KMETEC, E., and NEWCOMB, E. H. Am. Jour. Botany 43, 333 (1956).
LATIES, G. G. Plant Physiol. 28, 557 (1953).
LEHNINGER, A. L. *Harvey Lectures, 1955–56*, Academic Press, New York (1957).
LIEBERMAN, M. Science 127, 189 (1958).
LUND, H. A., VATTER, A. E., and HANSON, J. B. Jour. Biophys. Biochem. Cytol.
   4, 87, (1958).
MARTIN, E. M., and MORTON, R. K. Nature 176, 113 (1955).
MARTIN, E. M., and MORTON, R. K. Biochem. Jour. 62, 696 (1956a).
MARTIN, E. M., and MORTON, R. K. Biochem. Jour. 64, 221 (1956b).
MARTIN, E. M., and MORTON, R. K. Biochem. Jour. 64, 687 (1956c).
McCLENDON, J. F. Am. Jour. Botany 40, 260 (1953).
NEWCOMB, E. H. Proc. Soc. Exp. Biol. Med. 76, 504 (1951).
PALADE, G. E., in *Enzymes: Units of Biological Structure and Function* (H. O.
   GAEBLER, ed.), Academic Press, New York (1956).
ROTHSTEIN, A. Soc. Exp. Biol. Symposia 8, 165 (1954).
RUBIN, B. A., and LADYGINA, M. E. Doklady Akad. Nauk. S.S.S.R. 109, 361
   (1956).
SCHNEIDER, W. C., and HOGEBOOM, G. Ann. Rev. Biochem. 25, 201 (1956).
SETTERFIELD, G., STERN, H., and JOHNSTON, F. B. Can. J. Botany 37, 66 (1959).
SISSAKIAN, N. M., BEKINA, R. M., and MOSOLOVA, I. M. Proc. Acad. Sci. U.S.S.R.
   Biochem. 112, 27 (1957).
SISSAKIAN, N. M., VASIL'EVA, N. A., and SPIRIDONOVA, G. I. Biokhimiya 22, 813
   (1957b).
SISSAKIAN, N. M. Adv. in Enzymol. 20, 201 (1958).
SMILLIE, R. M. Australian Jour. Sci. 17, 217 (1955).
SMILLIE, R. M. Australian Jour. Biol. Sci. 9, 81 (1956a).
SMILLIE, R. M. Australian Jour. Biol. Sci. 9, 339 (1956b).
SMILLIE, R. M. Australian Jour. Biol. Sci. 9, 347 (1956c).
STAFFORD, H. A. Physiol. Plant. 4, 696 (1951).

STERN, H., and MIRSKY, A. E. Jour. Gen. Physiol. 36, 181 (1952).

T'SO, P. O., BONNER, J., and VINOGRAD, J. Jour. Biophys. and Biochem. Cytol. 2, 451 (1956).

VON KORFF, R. W. Arch. Biochem. Biophys. 31, 467 (1959).

WEBSTER, G. C. Am. Jour. Botany 39, 739 (1952).

WEBSTER, G. C. Nitrogen Metabolism in Plants, Row, Peterson, Evanston, Ill. (1959).

WHALEY, W. G., KEPHART, J. E., and MOLLENHAUER, H. H. Am. Jour. Botany 46, 743 (1959a).

WHALEY, W. G., MOLLENHAUER, H. H., and KEPHART, J. E. Jour. Biophys. Biochem. Cytol. 5, 501 (1959b).

Part II

Relationships of Respiration to Other Processes in the Plant

Chapter 7

The Internal Regulation

of Respiratory Rates

In previous chapters the available evidence on the existence of biochemical reaction sequences and their operation in the respiration of plant cells has been reviewed. The mechanisms whereby ATP, reduced nucleotides, and useful precursors are produced have been discussed in some detail. It has long been evident that any functional value which respiration has must depend on the links whereby it is connected to endergonic reactions in the cells; it is now recognized that the above compounds are these links. In the following chapters the evidence for direct and indirect relationships of various physiological processes to the all-important one of respiration will be discussed. The first deals with the ways in which the process of respiration may be controlled by the pace of various endergonic reactions.

The rates of respiration of plant tissues may be increased to a degree by appropriate adjustments of external factors such as temperature, O_2 tension, and supply of substrate. At one time it seemed reasonable to think that the rate achieved under these circumstances was the maximum of which the tissue was intrinsically capable; the machinery was apparently operating at full capacity.

In recent years this picture of respiration uncontrolled except by the limits of its own enzymatic machinery has been greatly modified. On the one hand, evidence from physiological experiments has been forthcoming that plant cells are not so limited. The important observations, discussed in later sections, are that, even when optimal conditions are provided, immediate stimulations can be elicited by supplying salts, growth regulators, and other agents to selected tissues. Of more general occurrence, and frequently much more striking, are the stimulations brought about by minute amounts of uncoupling agents. Immediate increases in respiratory rates—several-fold increases in suitable tissues (Harley *et al.*, 1956; Beevers, 1953)—result from adding DNP in concentrations of less than 10^{-4} M at pH 5.0. On the other hand has come the recognition, at the biochemical level, of ways in which internal restraint may be placed on the progress of multistep reaction sequences so that they operate at levels well below full capacity. For a full review of this topic the Ciba volume on metabolic regulation (Wolstenholme and O'Connor, 1959) should be consulted. A valuable review on aspects of control of metabolic rates in plants is that of Laties (1957).

Some of these possibilities of rate control are indicated in Figure 16. Control of steps in one reaction sequence may be brought about by fluctuating levels of an intermediate in another. Thus the sensitivity of hexose phosphate isomerase to 6-phosphogluconate (Potter and Niemeyer, 1959) and particularly to erythrose-4-phosphate offers such a control point. Within an individual sequence, since coenzymes are reduced in stoichiometric amounts, the rate of their regeneration by ancillary oxidation systems can clearly limit the progress of the over-all reaction. The availability of inorganic cofactors such as Mg^{++} is also variable, since these are subject to complexing with other fluctuating constituents such as ATP (Lehninger, 1959). However, in recognizing these control points it should be emphasized that the most potent and important seems to be yet another, that afforded by the ADP + iP → ATP system (Johnson, 1941; Lynen, 1941). The basis for this regulation is the fact that ADP and inorganic phosphate are required as reactants both in the glycolytic sequence and in oxidative phosphorylation; for each mole of pyruvate produced from fructose-1,6-diphosphate, 2 moles of ADP must be provided as cosubstrate, and for each pair of electrons

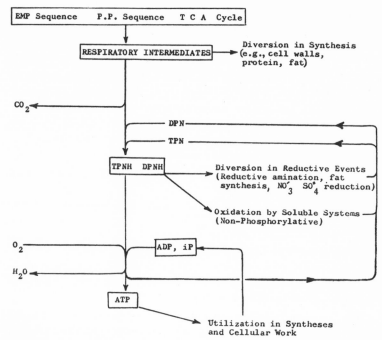

FIGURE 16.—Control of respiration rates by turnover of coenzymes and ATP.

transferred from DPNH to O_2 by mitochondrial oxidation a further 3 moles of ADP and iP may be consumed. Now although inorganic phosphate is usually present in excess, the cell is endowed with only a limited amount of adenylates, and glycolysis would be brought to a standstill if all of the available adenylate were converted to ATP (Chapter 5). Of course, this situation is probably never achieved, since there appears to be some breakdown of ATP at all times. In fact the rate of ATP utilization, by determining the amount of $\sim$P acceptor (ADP), would in turn determine the rate of its production and thus govern the rates of glycolysis and electron transfer. Thus the onset of any process in the cell which consumed ATP (syntheses, growth, solute transfer; see subsequent chapters) would be expected to elicit a glycolytic stimulation, and when ATP turnover was low, the respiration rate would decrease in consequence.

When the cell is deprived of O_2, oxidative phosphorylation stops and all of the ADP produced by ATP utilization becomes available for the glycolytic reactions which, as a result, can proceed faster in anaerobic than in aerobic conditions. When O_2 is provided, ADP utilization in oxidative phosphorylation begins and the regulation of the rate of glycolysis by these aerobic events is reimposed.

These considerations go far toward accounting for another important aspect of regulation of respiration, that known as the "Pasteur effect." This was first investigated intensively in higher plants by F. F. Blackman and his school, and there is a bulky literature. The problems and experimental approaches are fully discussed by Blackman (1954), Thomas (1956), and Turner (1951); only a brief statement must suffice here.

When the concentration of O_2 round a plant tissue is increased from zero, the accumulation of fermentation products is progressively repressed; pyruvate is increasingly accommodated by the mechanism of oxidative breakdown until, at a particular concentration of O_2 known as the "extinction point," none of it is diverted to alcohol and CO_2. However, in many higher plant tissues the influence of the O_2 goes beyond this simple diversion. It has been shown that at the same time as this shift is occurring there is a progressive decline in the *rate* of carbohydrate dissimilation; i.e., a conservation of carbon occurs as a result of providing O_2. This is the Pasteur effect.

It should be noted that frequently the figures for carbohydrate utilization which form the basis for a decision on the operation of the Pasteur effect are not from actual analysis but are estimates from data on CO_2 output. On the assumption that for each mole of carbon lost as CO_2 in N_2 2 moles are converted to alcohol, a value of greater than 1/3 for the I/N ratio (CO_2 produced in N_2/CO_2 produced in air) has been taken as indicating a conservation of carbon by providing O_2.

The inadequacies in this approach are discussed critically by Thomas (1956). One of the difficulties is that the rate of CO_2 output in N_2 may show very wide fluctuations during the period of measurement (Blackman, 1954).

However, in some tissues, for example apple fruit (Blackman, 1954) and rice seedlings (Taylor, 1942), the rate of CO_2 output in N_2 clearly *exceeds* that in air ($I/N > 1$). In these, since carbohydrates are the source of the CO_2, no assumptions are necessary about other products of fermentation to make the qualitative statement that the Pasteur effect is operating. The *extent* of the conservation of carbohydrate can be gauged only when the amounts of other products of fermentation (alcohol, acetaldehyde, lactate) are also measured (Thomas, 1956).

In most plant tissues I/N is less than unity, and in these it becomes necessary to know how much carbon there is in the other products of fermentation before even a qualitative statement about the operation of the Pasteur effect is permissible. Of course, if the breakdown of carbohydrates in N_2 did lead exclusively to equimolar amounts of ethanol and CO_2, as indeed it does in some, a value of I/N greater than $1/3$ would show that the Pasteur effect was operating. Unfortunately, data from a distressingly large number of tissues show that the alcohol production falls far short of that predicted from the CO_2 output (James, 1953, p. 122). Whatever factors are invoked to rationalize these observations, the import to the present problem is plain; the carbon loss cannot be accurately estimated from CO_2 output alone. I/N ratios of less than 1 when these are unsupported by other information are not an adequate basis for a decision on the operation of the Pasteur effect.

As Turner (1951) points out, however, there are now a sufficient number of examples in which the rates of both alcohol and CO_2 production have been directly measured to show that the Pasteur effect is a widespread feature of the respiration of higher plants. The extent of the conservation due to O_2 varied from $1/3$ to $4/5$. In only a few tissues (germinating buckwheat seedlings, Ranson, 1949; and pea embyros, Meeuse, quoted by Goddard, 1948) does it appear to be inoperative.

Clearly the most satisfactory method of demonstrating a conserving effect of O_2 is to show by actual analysis that carbohydrate loss is less in air than in N_2. Such experiments require that representative samples be withdrawn from larger batches of material. Successful demonstrations of the Pasteur effect in higher plants by this unequivocal method have now been achieved by Fidler (1951) for apples, by Neal and Girton (1955) for corn seedlings, and by Oota (1957) for germinating seedlings of *Vigna sesquipedalis*.

It should be noted that when aerobic carbohydrate loss is calculated from CO_2 output, the losses due to diversion of intermediates in the synthesis of other permanent components are not included; these are taken into account when carbohydrate loss is directly measured. The fact that a conserving effect of O_2 is still apparent in the tissues mentioned above indicates that the Pasteur effect may be something more than the facilitation of synthetic events by the availability of O_2. In other tissues the drainage of respiratory intermediates in synthetic events may be so extensive as to offset any conserving effect of the O_2. Thus in the experiments of Meeuse with pea seedlings (Goddard, 1948), although a Pasteur effect might have been deduced from the figures on CO_2 at some stages in development, the carbohydrate analyses show that the losses in air and N_2 were the same. In Kandler's (1953) experiments on maize embryos, which are discussed below, large amounts of glucose were used in synthetic events, and Betz (1957) emphasizes the importance of taking this into account.

If, as we assume, there is some competition for ADP between the reactions of glycolysis and those of oxidative phosphorylation, direct evidence for the operation of control by this system might be expected to come from actual determination of levels of ADP, ATP, and iP in the tissues. Such determinations are of course subject to some errors, and local pools out of equilibrium with the rest of the cell would upset the results. No clear relationship between respiration rate and

TABLE XXIX

RATIO ADP/ATP IN MATURE PEA SEEDS IN O_2 AND N_2

(ROWAN, SEAMAN, AND TURNER, 1956)

Experiment	O_2	N_2
1	0.4	1.4
2	1.2	2.3
3	7.6	18.2
4	1.3	4.0

ATP or ADP levels was apparent in developing pea fruit (Rowan and Turner, 1957), but some encouraging evidence has been provided by Rowan et al. (1956). When pea seeds were transferred from O_2 to N_2, there was a decrease in the level of ATP and an increase in iP, so that the ratio ADP: ATP increased in every experiment (Table XXIX). Reversible changes in iP levels consistent with phosphorylative control have also been observed when pea-stem segments were transferred to nitrogen (Figure 17). In a very valuable recent review Lynen et al. (1959) discuss the importance of changes in iP in controlling the respiration of yeast.

Other very strong, though indirect, evidence comes from experiments with the uncoupling agents. The effect of these substances is to prevent the phosphorylation of ADP during oxidative phosphorylation (p. 125). ATP breakdown is unaffected, and the result is an increased availability of ADP. Thus the constraint which is normally placed on electron transfer is removed. Glycolytic reactions which are not directly affected by DNP respond strikingly to the increase in ADP. They may in fact be stimulated to such an extent that the oxidation system is incapable of coping with the extra pyruvate produced, and the result is that the excess is diverted to alcohol and CO_2 (Beevers, 1953).

It is clear from the effects on CO_2 output that the loss of carbohydrate is considerably increased by DNP; and when the alcohol production is also taken into account, the loss is considerably greater. In carrot tissue this rate was calculated to be more than three times that occurring in the control in

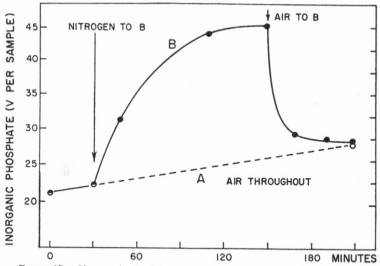

FIGURE 17.—Changes in the iP content of pea segments during a temporary experience in anaerobic conditions. (Beevers, unpublished.)

air. At critical DNP levels the rate of (aerobic) fermentation was at least as great as it was in N_2, and this at a point where aerobic respiration was being maintained at close to the control level (Figure 18).

In emphasizing the adequacy of the ~P transfer system as the primary basis for the Pasteur effect, the discussion of other possible mechanisms may be curtailed. The results with DNP make it most unlikely that aerobic glycolysis is held in check by a direct inhibitory effect of O_2, although inactivation of sensitive enzymes may occur *in vitro* (Turner and Mapson, 1958; Hatch and Turner, 1959). The suggestion of resynthesis of respiratory substrate from intermediates in the breakdown process, which was advanced as a most reasonable interpretation at a time when very little was known about metabolic pathways in plants and still less about their regulation (see Blackman, 1954), must now be regarded with informed skepticism. No direct evidence for its operation has

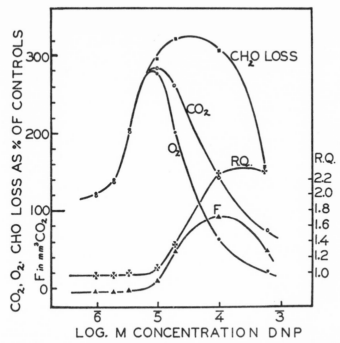

FIGURE 18.—The effect of DNP on the respiration of carrot slices. F is the component of the CO_2 output which can be ascribed to aerobic fermentation, and a corresponding amount of alcohol was allowed for in estimating the carbohydrate loss. (Beevers, 1953.)

been provided, and recent work with labeled intermediates has spoken strongly against it. The pertinent experiments here are those with labeled acids, particularly pyruvate. The synthesis of hexose units from such intermediates occurs only in specialized tissues such as green leaves in the light and in seedlings breaking down fatty reserves; it is noticeably lacking in a variety of other plant tissues (Neal and Beevers, 1960; James and Slater, 1959).

It should be noted that Forward (1951a,b) invokes oxidative anabolism in interpreting her extensive experiments with barley seedlings and has emphasized that, insofar as synthesis of cell components such as protein occurs more rapidly in aerobic conditions, this "oxidative assimilation" represents a conservation of carbon (see Barnell, 1937). It might be anticipated that drainage of respiratory intermediates destined for posts as tissue constituents would be greatest in actively growing material. When we also consider that the synthetic events resulting from this drainage are ones which are known to consume ATP, it is clear that glycolytic rates in air in such tissues are likely to be nearer to the maximum ones than in those older tissues in which ATP turnover is lower. As a result of extensive synthesis of cellular constituents the rate of carbohydrate utilization may be as great as it is under N_2, and thus the Pasteur effect would be at a minimum in such material. It follows, then, that one would anticipate a larger stimulation by DNP in older tissues. Such is indeed the case. The maximum stimulations observed are those in tissues in which ATP utilization can be deduced to be low (Harley et al., 1956), and in the most actively growing material the magnitude of the stimulations of O_2 uptake is less (Beevers, 1953). In a series of experiments with corn coleoptiles, castor-bean hypocotyls, and carrots a progressive increase was noted in the response to DNP as the tissues matured (Gaur, 1957). In carrots (Figure 19) the total capacity for respiration (as indicated by the maximum rate induced by DNP) remained essentially constant during growth, but the actual respiration declined from 100% of this value in the youngest tissue to some 30% of this in the oldest material. As the tissue ages, apparently the ATP turnover declines and there is a correspondingly increased restraint on the rate of glycolysis. Direct evidence of such a decreased supply of ADP in older tissues would be extremely valuable.

   Induced respiration in slices of storage tissue and the climacteric rise in fruits. When discs of underground storage tissue such as carrots, potatoes, artichoke, and chicory are aerated at moderate temperatures, their respiration rate rises gradually over a period of several hours until it reaches a level from two to five times that of the freshly cut material. A variety of inhibitors prevent the development of this rise (see

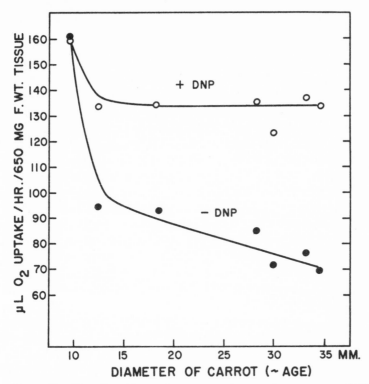

FIGURE 19.—The effect of age of carrot-root tissue on its response to DNP. The solid circles show the declining rate of respiration/unit fresh weight as the root ages. The open circles show the maximum rates achieved at each stage by treatment with the most effective concentration of DNP. (Gaur and Beevers, unpublished.)

Laties, 1957, 1959a,b). The induced respiration has some qualitative differences from that of fresh tissue, and it now seems clear that one of these changes is an increased participation of the pentose phosphate pathway (ap Rees and Beevers, 1960). It is significant that chloramphenicol, an inhibitor of protein synthesis, prevents the increase in respiration (Calo *et al.*, 1957), and it is clear that some enzyme synthesis occurs during the rise. For example, Hackett and Haas (1958) have shown that the activities of DPNH oxidase (sensitive to cyanide) and some cytochrome components increase when potato discs are aerated, and Marrè (1960) has shown that glucose-6-phosphate dehydrogenase activity increases during this time. In the potato, Thimann *et al.* have emphasized that, when the induced respiration has developed, the cyanide sensitivity is lowered. MacDonald (1959) has recently provided extensive data on changes in sensitivity to a variety of inhibitors during prolonged washing periods. However, at least in some tissues, e.g., carrot, the respiratory rise begins well before the cyanide resistance develops. Thus there does not seem to be a causal connection between the two events.

The full capacity for respiration is clearly not realized before the induced respiration begins, because the addition of DNP at the outset leads to a stimulation of respiration which is quantitatively similar to that induced by aging. After the development of the induced respiration, DNP produces at best a very small further stimulation. However, this is patently not due to the production of some natural uncoupler; the abilities of the slices to esterify inorganic phosphate, to carry out a variety of synthetic processes, and to accumulate salts and sugars all increase strikingly during the respiratory rise.

The changing response to DNP thus seems to be best explained by supposing that originally the respiratory rate of the discs is restrained by the ADP supply (ATP turnover) but that an increasing rate of ATP turnover removes this limitation as the slices are aerated. The increased participation of the pentose phosphate pathway is tentatively ascribed to an increased utilization of TPNH (ap Rees and Beevers, 1960; Butt and Beevers, 1960). The synthesis of new protein and other cell constituents—the beginnings of growth—may be the major events utilizing ATP, TPNH, and intermediates, and the trigger the exposure of potentially growing cells to a more conducive environment. The anomalous inhibitor and reversal effects described by Laties (1959a,b) in chicory remain unexplained and emphasize that problems remain in the complete elucidation of induced respiration.

Similar considerations apply to the climacteric rise in respiration which occurs in many fruits (Biale, 1951; Hulme, 1958). Here again the capacity to respond to DNP is lost during the rise (Pearson and Robertson, 1954; Millerd *et al.*, 1953; Neal and Hulme, 1958). Hulme (1954, 1958) and Rowan *et al.* (1958) have shown that increased ATP turnover is a more reasonable explanation of the spontaneous respiratory rise than uncoupling (Millerd *et al.*, 1953). Phosphate incorporation into organic forms (Marks *et al.*, 1957) and protein synthesis (Hulme, 1954; Pearson and Robertson, 1954; Rowan *et al.*, 1958) both occur during the respiratory rise, and Hulme (1958) suggests that new respiratory enzymes may be produced. We are thus led to conclude that, as in the carrot slices, some different channeling of intermediates (Tager, 1956) may occur in the respiration which is brought about by an increased turnover of ATP. The further understanding of these changes must include the relationship to ancillary events in the fruit during climacteric; the natural trigger which determines the timing of the climacteric and the effectiveness of ethylene in inducing the respiratory rise are not understood at present.

REFERENCES

AP REES, T., and BEEVERS, H. Plant Physiol. 35, 839 (1960).
BARNELL, H. R. Proc. Roy. Soc. B123, 321 (1937).
BEEVERS, H. Am. Jour. Botany 40, 91 (1953).
BEEVERS, H. Unpublished results (1956).
BETZ, A. Planta 50, 122 (1957).
BIALE, J. B. Ann. Rev. Plant. Physiol. 2, 183 (1951).
BLACKMAN, F. F. *Analytic Studies on Plant Respiration*, Cambridge Univ. Press (1954).
BUTT, V. S., and BEEVERS, H. Biochem. Jour. 76, 51P (1960).
CALO, N., MARKS, J., and VARNER, J. E. Nature 180, 1142 (1957).
FIDLER, J. C. Jour. Exp. Botany 2, 41 (1951).
FORWARD, D. F. New Phytol. 50, 297 (1951a).
FORWARD, D. F. New Phytol. 50, 325 (1951b).
GAUR, B. K. Ph.D. Thesis, Purdue University, Lafayette, Indiana (1957).
GODDARD, D. R. Growth 12, 17 (1948).
HACKETT, D. P., and HAAS, D. W. Plant Physiol. 335, vii (1958).
HARLEY, J. L., and SMITH, D. C. Ann. Botany 20, 513 (1956).
HARLEY, J. L., McCREADY, C. C., BRIERLEY, J. K., and JENNINGS, D. H. New Phytol. 55, 1 (1956).
HATCH, M. C., and TURNER, J. F. Biochem. Jour. 72, 524 (1959).
HULME, A. C. Jour. Exp. Botany 5, 159 (1954).

HULME, A. C. Adv. in Food Research **8,** 297 (1958).
JAMES, W. O. *Plant Respiration,* Clarendon Press, Oxford (1953).
JAMES, W. O., and RITCHIE, A. Proc. Roy. Soc. **B143,** 302 (1955).
JAMES, W. O., and SLATER, W. G. Proc. Roy. Soc. **B150,** 192 (1959).
JOHNSON, M. J. Science **94,** 200 (1941).
KANDLER, O. Naturforschung **86,** 109 (1953).
LATIES, G. G. Survey of Biological Progress **3,** 215 (1957).
LATIES, G. G. Arch. Biochem. Biophys. **79,** 364 (1959a).
LATIES, G. G. Arch. Biochem. Biophys. **79,** 378 (1959b).
LEHNINGER, A. L., in *Developmental Cytology* (D. RUDNICK, ed.), Ronald Press, New York (1959).
LYNEN, F. Ann. Chem. **546,** 120 (1941).
LYNEN, F., HARTMAN, G., NETTER, K. F., and SCHUEGRAF, A., in Ciba Foundation Symposium, *Regulation of Cell Metabolism* (G. E. W. WOLSTENHOLME and C. M. O'CONNOR, eds.), Churchill, London (1959).
MACDONALD, J. R. Ann. Botany (N.S.) **23,** 241 (1959).
MARKS, J. D., BERNLOHR, R., and VARNER, J. E. Plant Physiol. **32,** 259 (1957).
MARRÈ, E. Personal communication (1960).
MILLERD, A., BONNER, J., and BIALE, J. B. Plant Physiol. **28,** 521 (1953).
NEAL, G. E., and BEEVERS, H. Biochem. Jour. **74,** 409 (1960).
NEAL, G. E., and HULME, A. C. Jour. Exp. Botany **9,** 403 (1958).
NEAL, M. J., and GIRTON, R. E. Am. Jour. Botany **42,** 733 (1955).
OOTA, Y. Physiol. Plant. **10,** 910 (1957).
PEARSON, J. A., and ROBERTSON, R. N. Australian Jour. Biol. Sci. **7,** 1 (1954).
POTTER, V. R., and NIEMEYER, H., in Ciba Foundation Symposium, *Regulation of Cell Metabolism* (G. E. W. WOLSTENHOLME and C. M. O'CONNOR, eds.), Churchill, London (1959).
RANSON, S. L. Ph.D. Thesis, Durham, England (1949).
ROWAN, K. S., SEAMAN, D. E., and TURNER, J. S. Nature, **177,** 333 (1956).
ROWAN, K. S., and TURNER, D. H. Australian Jour. Biol. Sci. **10,** 302 (1957).
ROWAN, K. S., PRATT, H. K., and ROBERTSON, R. N. Australian Jour. Biol. Sci. **11,** 329 (1958).
TAGER, J. M. S. African Jour. Sci. **53,** 167 (1956).
TAYLOR, D. L. Am. Jour. Botany **29,** 721 (1942).
THIMANN, K. V., YOCUM, C. S., and HACKETT, D. P. Arch. Biochem. Biophys. **53,** 239 (1954).
THOMAS, M., RANSON, S. L., and RICHARDSON, J. A. *Plant Physiology* (4th ed.), Churchill, London (1956).
TURNER, J. F., and MAPSON, L. W. Nature **181,** 170 (1958).
TURNER, J. S. Ann. Rev. Plant Physiol. **2,** 145 (1951).
WOLSTENHOLME, G. E. W., and O'CONNOR, C. M. (eds.). Ciba Foundation Symposium, *Regulation of Cell Metabolism,* Churchill, London (1959).

Chapter 8

Respiration in Relation

to Solute Transfer

The uptake of solutes from the environment and movements of organic and inorganic molecules from cell to cell are
essential to the economy of the higher plant. Not all of this
transfer is dependent on the metabolism of the cells concerned, but a great deal of work has been carried out on one
aspect of absorption which is certainly related to respiration,
i.e., the accumulation of salts, particularly in excised roots
and discs of storage tissues such as carrot and potato. This
ability of plant cells to accumulate materials in their vacuoles
against an apparent concentration gradient is not limited to
inorganic salts or to the tissues mentioned above. Some emphasis has been laid on accumulation in cortical regions of
roots as an important stage in the transfer of salts from the
nutrient solution to the xylem elements. Now it seems clear
that, so far as long-range transport is concerned, this movement into vacuoles, though inevitable, may be strictly diver-
sionary and reversible only under stress. Salts may be transported across the cortex along pathways which do not include
the vacuole, and under some conditions of rapid water uptake there may be an accelerated transfer of salts. This is not
to say that metabolic processes play no role in transport to
the xylem; it is clear from inhibitor treatments and the
maintenance of a concentration difference between the xylem
and the outside solution that they do (Brouwer, 1956).

The position taken here is that the metabolic reactions essential to active transfer, whether this is into the protoplast
or the vacuole, across the protoplasmic continuum, or into

vascular elements, may all be aspects of a similar theme. Thus the relationship to respiration may justifiably be considered at the cellular level.

We should distinguish first between the nonmetabolic uptake of solutes—the "passive permeation" of Epstein (1955)—which occurs into regions of the tissue which come into ready equilibrium with the outside medium, and the process of metabolic uptake, which, by contrast, may continue indefinitely and against an apparent concentration gradient (Epstein, 1956). Metabolic uptake has a characteristically high temperature coefficient (Hoagland, 1948). It is, moreover, selective; certain ions are accumulated more readily than others, while some may in fact be excluded (see Hoagland, 1948; Collander, 1939). It is now generally agreed that it is not necessary to include an appreciable part of the protoplasm in the volume of the tissue with which inorganic salts rapidly equilibrate, and that the so-called "free space" ends at the outer protoplasmic surface. However, in the walls and on the protoplasmic surface there are (predominantly negatively charged) exchange spots onto which ions may be adsorbed. This adsorption is not a prerequisite to entry into the root and will be related to respiration only insofar as the production of these nonspecific binding sites is under metabolic control. It is noticeable particularly when a change is made in the ionic environment, since this in turn brings about a change in the distribution of the adsorbed ion complement. The contribution of this and other simple physical considerations to progressive salt accumulation can be judged to be small from the fact that continued uptake can frequently be completely abolished by interfering with aerobic metabolism (see below). Indeed, several authors use "uptake" synonymously with "accumulation."

The importance of the process of vacuolation to the ability of cells to accumulate salts has been brought out by Brown and Cartwright (1953), who measured salt uptake of cells at different developmental stages. The youngest meristematic cells absorbed salts less readily than vacuolated ones. Steward and Millar (1954) have emphasized that in the youngest cells much of the salt absorbed may be used in the synthesis of new components or bound on sites produced in the synthesis of new protein. In vacuolated cells, on the other hand, these reactions are at a minimum, and transfer to the vacuole is the major fate.

EVIDENCE LINKING ACCUMULATION WITH RESPIRATION

Effects of O_2 tension. Steward (1932) was the first to emphasize the stimulatory effect of adequate aeration on the ability of tissues to accumulate salts, and the requirement for aerobic respiration has been repeatedly observed. Curves showing parallelism between salt accumulation and respiration as a function of O_2 tension have been provided for some tissues (e.g., Steward, 1932; Hammond *et al.*, 1955; Harley *et al.*, 1956; Hopkins, 1956).

Effects of inhibitors (Table XXX). In general it is found that whenever respiration (O_2 uptake) is interfered with, the concomitant salt accumulation is at least as severely curtailed. Great stress has been laid on the adverse effects of the oxidase inhibitors azide and cyanide (Robertson and Turner, 1945; Weeks and Robertson, 1950; Lundegårdh, 1955a,b; Middleton, 1955, 1956; Ordin and Jacobson, 1955), and it is important to note that these agents inhibit salt uptake strongly even in tissues whose respiration is resistant to (Osterlind, 1951) or even stimulated by these reagents (Harley *et al.*, 1956). It has also been established that CO inhibits salt accumulation in a variety of tissues (Weeks and Robertson, 1950; Ordin and Jacobson, 1955; Honda, 1956; Middleton, 1955), and the inhibitions have been successfully reversed by light in some experiments (Table XXX).

When these observations are considered alongside the spectrophotometric demonstrations of Lundegårdh (1955b), there can be no doubt that respiration mediated by cytochrome oxidase is involved in salt accumulation. However, this evidence alone is certainly inadequate to impute any special role to the cytochrome system. Thus inhibitors of enzymes of glycolysis or the TCA cycle slow down O_2 uptake and produce striking inhibitions of salt uptake as well (see Machlis, 1944; Stenlid,

TABLE XXX

INHIBITORS OF SALT UPTAKE* BY BARLEY ROOTS

(ORDIN AND JACOBSON, 1955)

INHIBITOR	CONCENTRATION	% INHIBITION	
		K+ Uptake	Br' Uptake
Fluoride	0.04 M	97	60
Iodoacetate	0.001 M	81	65
Arsenite	0.0001 M	60	75
Fluoroacetate	0.005 M	72	64
Trans-aconitate	0.02 M	63	47
Malonate	0.005 M	40	42
Cyanide	0.002 M	74	74
CO (dark)	95% (O_2 = 5%)	100	97
CO (light)	95% (O_2 = 5%)	8	0
DNP	0.000001 M	90	67
Arsenate	0.0002 M	74	63

* Potassium bromide, 0.005 N.

1949; Ordin and Jacobson, 1955). It was stressed that uptake of salt was more sensitive to several of the compounds than was respiration.

A most revealing response is that to the uncoupling agent DNP (Robertson et al., 1951; Harley et al., 1956). It is found that as the concentration of DNP is increased from an innocuous level and the rate of O_2 uptake is increased, the rate of salt uptake, far from rising, begins to decline quite sharply and may be reduced to less than half its original rate while the respiration is maximally stimulated to a level more than twice that of the controls (Figure 20). Further inhibition ensues as the concentration is still further increased. It is emphasized, in anticipation of later discussion, that the stimulated respiration brought about by DNP is mediated by the cytochrome system (Figure 21).

It should be noted that an alternative explanation is sometimes advanced to explain the striking effects of anaerobiosis and respiratory inhibitors. This is that the uptake and retention of ions depend strictly on the maintenance of membrane

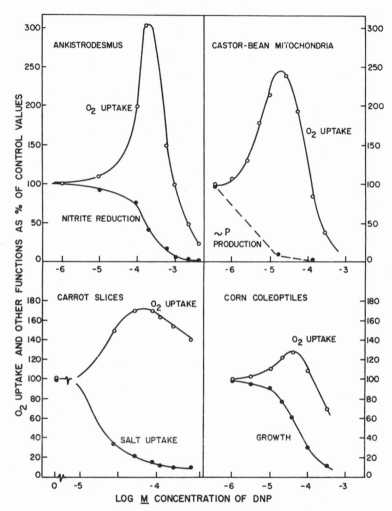

FIGURE 20.—The effects of DNP on O_2 uptake and associated processes. *Upper left*, nitrite reduction in *Ankistrodesmus* (after Kessler, 1955). *Upper right*, ATP production by mitochondria. (Gaur and Beevers, 1959; Akazawa and Beevers, 1957.) *Lower left*, salt uptake (after Robertson, *et al.* 1951). *Lower right*, elongation of corn coleoptiles (French and Beevers, 1953).

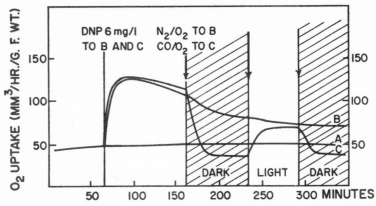

FIGURE 21.—Effects of DNP and CO on respiration of carrot slices. All gas mixtures contained 6.5% O_2. Note that the DNP-stimulated respiration is photoreversibly inhibited by CO (after Robertson *et al.*, 1951).

structure and that the treatments retarding salt uptake do so by weakening or destroying this structure. There can of course be no quarrel with the essentiality of intact and functional protoplasmic membranes, but two points in favor of the view that the effects are more biochemical than structural are (1) the ready reversibility of the effects of some inhibitors and anaerobiosis and (2) the fact that previously accumulated ions may be retained in the presence of the inhibitors and in N_2.

Salt-stimulated respiration. When "low-salt" barley roots (Hoagland 1948; Lundegårdh, 1955b; Handley and Overstreet, 1955), well-washed carrot discs (Robertson and Turner, 1945), and a variety of other plant materials with highly vacuolated cells (Honda, 1956) are transferred from distilled water to dilute salt solutions, they begin to absorb ions, and at the same time their respiration (O_2 uptake and CO_2 output) may be noticeably stimulated. The salt-induced respiration is abolished by cyanide and carbon monoxide. This phenomenon is of interest in itself, as it indicates the release of some constraint on the respiratory process (see pp. 148 ff.). However, great importance has been attached to it as possibly indicating a bringing into play of a respiratory component particularly involved in the actual process of accumulation

(Lundegårdh, 1955a, 1958a). It is important to note, first of all, that salt accumulation frequently occurs without a concomitant stimulation of respiration and that, even in responsive material, the magnitude of the response depends greatly on what ions are offered and what the complementary ions are (Handley and Overstreet, 1955). Secondly, and particularly in view of the importance that Lundegårdh attaches to the anion component, it is of interest that the stimulation can be induced when absorption of anions is precluded by supplying the cation absorbed on an exchange resin (Epstein, 1954; Handley and Overstreet, 1955).

THE MECHANISM OF ACCUMULATION

An acceptable mechanism must account for (a) the distinctively selective pattern of transfer of ions across the outer protoplasmic barrier, (b) the deposition of these ions at points in the protoplasm or the vacuole from which they do not freely return, and (c) the close relationship with respiration.

Most recent suggestions have centered upon the concept that at the protoplasmic surface the ion being transported becomes attracted electrically to a specific absorption site or attached to some chemical component which may be part of a recognizable subcellular structure. In this combination the complexed or adsorbed ion is able to pierce the erstwhile barrier to its free movement. It may be deposited when by chance it arrives at some point where the conditions are sufficiently different to induce a breakdown of the association or a transfer of the ion to some other acceptor. Without necessarily committing themselves to the existence of actual chemical entities, many authors in this field speak of these agents by which transport is achieved as "carriers" (see Laties, 1959).

We will discuss briefly the degree to which some of Lundegårdh's suggestions and alternative explanations satisfy the requirements listed above. Lundegårdh's scheme for ion accumulation, which has justifiably attracted a great deal of attention, has appeared in several forms as new evidence has been gathered (see Lundegårdh, 1955a,b, 1958a,b). The central theme, however, remains the same, namely, that as electrons from respiratory intermediates pass through the electron-transfer sequence terminating with cytochrome oxidase there is a corresponding inward passage of anions. The anions are pictured as entering some form of temporary attachment with the oxidized forms of the cytochromes and other members of the sequence, and at each stage an anion takes the place of an electron as it is moved to the next component. The cations are thought to move in passively in amounts electrically balancing the anions transferred. The maximum rate of anion uptake would be expected when for each electron being converted to water in the respiration an anion was transported. That is to say, the ratio of monovalent ions transported/mole O_2 absorbed in respiration would equal 4 in the best possible case (Figure 22). When this ratio has been measured experimentally (see below), only the O_2 uptake of the salt-induced respiration has been used, with doubtful justification. It is implied that whatever respiration is occurring before the salt is added is incapable of supporting salt accumulation. In well-washed carrot slices whose respiration has reached the basal level, this is perhaps more likely to be so than in other materials.

The following evidence can be cited in support:

a. The importance of the cytochrome system in respiration and salt accumulation as shown by inhibitor studies.

b. The spectrophotometric changes, showing rapid oxidation of reduced respiratory components when salts are added to living wheat roots in distilled water (Lundegårdh, 1955a).

c. The existence of salt respiration, which is ascribed to a facilitation of outward electron flow by the act of providing anions which can be moved inward in exchange for electrons.

d. The demonstration that, under certain conditions, the theoretical value of 4 for the ratio given above is approached (Robertson and Wilkins, 1948).

Although a distinction is frequently made between Lundegårdh's scheme and other so-called "carrier" theories, it will

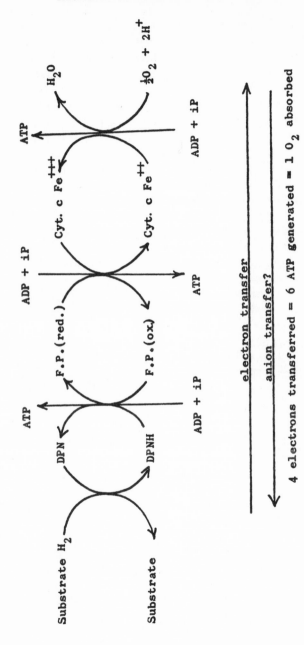

FIGURE 22.—Possible relations between electron transfer and anion uptake.

be seen that the cytochromes can themselves be regarded as carriers. The realization that the cytochromes are strictly located on the mitochondria prompted Robertson (1957) to suggest, in an extension of Lundegårdh's theory, that the attachment to respiratory catalysts followed by bodily movement of the organelles housing them might be substituted for Lundegårdh's electron ladder, permanently and providentially orientated with the cytochrome oxidase at the protoplasmic surface. Some evidence in favor of the mitochondria as selective binding agents has indeed been provided (Robertson *et al.*, 1955). Recent suggestions of Lundegårdh's (1955a,b) are that the anions introduced by the cytochrome sequence become associated with more specific carriers at points more remote from the protoplasmic surface. Alternatively, selectivity may be impressed before association with the cytochromes, which are held to be responsible for a metabolic steering through the bulk of the protoplasm (Lundegårdh, 1958b).

It is important that several authors hold very different views on the explanation of salt-induced respiration, which is the cornerstone of the theory. First, it has been established that when salts are added to enzymes of the cytochrome chain (Miller and Evans, 1956) and the intact DPNH–cytochrome oxidase system (Honda, Robertson, and Gregory, 1958), the O_2 uptake is strikingly stimulated. These stimulations, observed under conditions where salt transport is not involved, are considered by Honda and his colleagues to be large enough to account for the phenomenon of salt-induced respiration. It is also apparent from the fact that maximal stimulation of respiration occurs at lower levels of salt than are required for maximum rates of salt accumulation that the two processes are not simply related, and it is highly significant that salt respiration may persist for several hours after the salt is removed (e.g., Handley and Overstreet, 1955; Robertson and Thorn, 1945). Clearly the respiratory increase on adding a salt could be a consequence of its utilization in metabolism (Becking, 1956); the stimulation of some synthetic process by the entering ions with a resulting increase in the ATP turnover would produce the observed result. (Nitrate is considered especially in this regard on p. 180).

A strong argument against Lundegårdh's proposals would be the observation of higher efficiencies than those predicted. Lundegårdh (1958b) emphasizes that high values may be expected in the early phase of salt absorption and stresses the importance of taking the "idling" due to internally mobile anions into account. Handley and Overstreet (1955) have reported values greater than 4 obtained over longer periods for this critical ratio. However, the respiration of the roots in the absence of added salt ("idling" of Lundegårdh) was high in relation to that induced by the salt, and it does not seem reasonable to treat this as basal respiration incapable of supporting salt absorption (see above).

A more compelling argument against the contention that electron flow through the cytochrome system is a sufficient basis for accumulation of salts are the opposite responses of salt uptake and O_2 uptake to DNP mentioned above (Table XXXI, Figure 20). These results with DNP in fact point to a dependence not on electron transport per se but on the phosphorylations which are normally geared to it (Robertson et al., 1951; Sutcliffe and Hackett, 1957). A function for ATP might well be found in the production or maintenance of carriers (specific for groups of ions) of the kind suggested by other approaches to this problem (Epstein, 1956). The dependence of salt accumulation on respiration would thus be ascribed to the mediation of the same energy-transfer system as that which is recognized to be responsible for other kinds of cellular work, and the increased turnover of ATP during salt uptake would contribute to salt-stimulated respiration (Harley et al., 1956; Laties, 1957, 1959; Sutcliffe and Hackett, 1957). The capacity of respiration to support salt accumulation would, on this basis, be better described by the amount of ATP produced than by the electron flow itself (Figure 22), and the stimulatory effects of light in the absence of CO_2 fixation (Arisz, 1956; van Lookeren Campagne, 1957) might be ascribed to photophosphorylation. A similar interpretation of

TABLE XXXI

Some of the Processes in Plants Which are Inhibited by
DNP at Levels Which Stimulate Respiration

Process	Tissue	Authors
Uptake and transport:		
Salt accumulation	Carrot discs	Robertson *et al.* (1951)
	Beech roots	Harley *et al.* (1956)
	Barley roots	Ordin and Jacobson (1955)
Glucose uptake	Tobacco-leaf discs	Pennell and Weatherley (1958)
	Wheat roots	Stenlid (1949)
	Carrot discs	Gaur and Beevers (1959)
Acetate, succinate, glucose uptake	Corn root tips	Humphreys and Dugger (1959)
Amino acid accumulation	Carrot discs	Birt and Hird (1956)
Auxin uptake	Oat coleoptiles	Johnson and Bonner (1956)
Phosphate uptake and esterification	Barley roots	Loughman and Russell (1957)
Transport of salts, amino acids, and amides	*Drosera* tentacles	Arisz (1953)
Phloem transport	*Pelargonium*	Willenbrink (1957)
Polar transport of auxins	Sunflower stem	Niedergang-Kamien and Leopold (1957)
Salt movement into xylem	Bean roots	Brouwer (1956)
Metabolic interconversions:		
Incorporation of glutamate into protein	Several	Webster (1954)
Ammonia assimilation, glutamine synthesis	Barley roots	Yemm and Willis (1956)
Acetate → Fat	Peanut cotyledons	Newcomb and Stumpf (1955)
Sucrose → Chlorogenic acid	Sunflower seedlings	Ruckenbrod (1954)
Sucrose → Anthocyanin	Saxifrage leaves	Eberhart (1954)
Fat → Sugar	Castor-bean seedlings	Cresta *et al.* (1953)
Sugars → Starch	*Brassica* leaves	Maruo *et al.* (1953)
	Tobacco leaves	Porter and Runeckles (1956)
Reduction of nitrite	*Ankistrodesmus*	Kessler (1955)

Table XXXI—*Continued*

Process	Tissue	Authors
Other physiological changes:		
Growth	Coleoptiles, roots, storage tissue	Many
Fruit ripening	Tomato	Marks *et al.* (1957); Spencer (1959)
Ethylene production in fruit	Mature green tomato	Spencer (1959)
Stomatal opening	*Stizolobium* leaves	Ventura (1954)

the effects of light on glucose uptake will be recalled (Kandler, 1954).

Another aspect of the interrelations between respiration and salt uptake is that shown under conditions where more of the supplied cation than the anion is absorbed. The "excess cation absorption" occurs when a mobile cation, such as potassium, is supplied with a less mobile anion, such as sulphate. Ulrich (1941) demonstrated that the metabolism of barley roots under these circumstances undergoes a significant change; the most obvious manifestation is a decrease in R.Q., and this is accompanied by an increase in the organic acid content of the roots. The excess cation absorption is balanced by the accumulating acid, and reverse changes occur during the excess anion absorption.

In later work with $C^{14}O_2$ and excised barley roots (Poel, 1953; Jacobson and Ordin, 1954; Jacobson, 1955), it was shown that CO_2 fixation was markedly influenced by the nutrient composition of the ambient solution. When this was such that excess cation absorption occurred, the fixation of $C^{14}O_2$ was strikingly increased. Further, the fixed $C^{14}O_2$ was shown to be predominantly in -COOH groups of malic acid. It seems, therefore, that the ability of a tissue to accommodate an excess of cations may be related to its ability to fix CO_2 (or HCO_3' anions), and, to the extent that this occurs, acid accumulation and a decreased R.Q. might be anticipated.

Respiratory energy may be utilized also in the uptake and

transfer of solutes other than inorganic ions (Table XXXI). Thus, glucose uptake by a variety of tissues is demonstrably more than a simple diffusion process. It can proceed until the medium is free of glucose, it is sensitive to temperature and O_2 tension, and it is curtailed by respiratory inhibitors, related sugars, and DNP. Birt and Hird (1956, 1958) have shown that the accumulation of amino acids by carrot discs has similar characteristics, and the uptake and transport of growth-regulating substances such as indoleacetic acid (Reinhold, 1954) can be ascribed in large part to metabolic transport. Transport in phloem is also sensitive to respiratory inhibitors and DNP (Willenbrink, 1957), and it is tempting to suppose that the high rates of movement are brought about by the participation of respiratory energy. The work of Arisz (1953) on transport in *Drosera* tentacles is also of interest here (Table XXXI).

In mycorrhizal roots of beech, Harley and his colleagues (1956, 1958) have shown that respiration may be increased as a result of the act of glucose accumulation (i.e., a response distinct from utilization of the glucose as respiratory substrate) and that this stimulation is similar to that induced by salts and further by DNP. These authors suggest that all of these stimulations have a common explanation, i.e., an increased availability of ADP at the respiratory control centers (Chapter 7). This would be brought about by DNP acting as an uncoupler and by the increased utilization of ATP in the accumulation of the salt and glucose. Middleton (1956) has also shown that respiratory stimulations are induced in carrot and beet slices by salts, glucose, and DNP.

Another aspect of vacuolar concentration is that of organic acids produced in metabolism. There are now good indications that respiratory energy is expended in maintaining vacuolar and protoplasmic pools out of equilibrium with each other (Stiller, 1959). It has long been known (Bennet-Clark and Bexon, 1943) that the addition of small amounts of organic acids may stimulate the respiration of tissues which already contain (in their vacuoles) larger amounts of the same acids. It would be of interest to determine whether metabolic transport of the added acid contributed to the stimulations observed.

REFERENCES

AKAZAWA, T., and BEEVERS, H. Biochem. Jour. **67**, 115 (1957).
ARISZ, W. H. Acta Botanica Neerland. **2**, 74 (1953).
ARISZ, W. H. Protoplasma **46**, 5 (1956).
BECKING, J. H. Acta Botanica Neerland. **5**, 1 (1956).
BENNET-CLARK, T. A., and BEXON, D. New Phytol. **42**, 65 (1943).
BIRT, L. M., and HIRD, F. J. R. Biochem. Jour. **64**, 305 (1956).
BIRT, L. M., and HIRD, F. J. R. Biochem. Jour. **70**, 277 (1958).
BROUWER, R. Acta Botanica Neerland. **5**, 287 (1956).
BROWN, R., and CARTWRIGHT, P. M. Jour. Exp. Botany **4**, 197 (1953).
COLLANDER, R. Protoplasma **33**, 215 (1939).
CRESTA, M., SPADONI, M. A., and TECCE, G. Quaderni nutriz. **13**, 43 (1953).
EBERHART, F. Planta **43**, 253 (1954).
EPSTEIN, E. Science **120**, 987 (1954).
EPSTEIN, E. Plant Physiol. **30**, 529 (1955).
EPSTEIN, E. Ann. Rev. Plant Physiol. **7**, 1 (1956).
FRENCH, R. C., and BEEVERS, H. Am. J. Botany **40**, 660 (1953).
GAUR, B. K., and BEEVERS, H. Plant Physiol. **34**, 427 (1959).
HAMMOND, L. C., ALLAWAY, W. H., and LOOMIS, W. E. Plant Physiol. **30**, 155 (1955).
HANDLEY, R., and OVERSTREET, R. Plant Physiol. **30**, 418 (1955).
HARLEY, J. L., and JENNINGS, D. H. Proc. Roy. Soc. B**148**, 403 (1958).
HARLEY, J. L., McCREADY, C. C., BRIERLEY, J. K., and JENNINGS, D. H. New Phytol. **55**, 1 (1956).
HOAGLAND, D. R. Lectures on the Inorganic Nutrition of Plants, Chronica Botanica, Waltham, Mass. (1948).
HONDA, S. I. Plant Physiol. **31**, 62 (1956).
HONDA, S. I., ROBERTSON, R. N., and GREGORY, J. M. Australian Jour. Biol. Sci. **11**, 1 (1958).
HOPKINS, H. T. Plant Physiol. **31**, 155 (1956).
HUMPHREYS, T. E., and DUGGER, W. M. Plant Physiol. **34**, 112 (1959).
JACOBSON, L., and ORDIN, L. Plant Physiol. **29**, 70 (1954).
JACOBSON, L. Plant Physiol. **30**, 264 (1955).
JOHNSON, M. P., and BONNER, J. Physiol. Plant. **9**, 102 (1956).
KANDLER, O. Z. Naturforsch. **9b**, 625 (1954).
KESSLER, E. Planta **45**, 94 (1955).
LATIES, G. G. Survey of Biol. Progress **3**, 215 (1957).
LATIES, G. G. Ann. Rev. Plant Physiol. **10**, 87 (1959).
LOUGHMAN, G., and RUSSELL, R. S. Jour. Exp. Botany **8**, 280 (1957).
LUNDEGÅRDH, H. Ann. Rev. Plant Physiol. **6**, 1 (1955a).
LUNDEGÅRDH, H. Soc. Exp. Biol. Symposia **8**, 262 (1955b).
LUNDEGÅRDH, H., in Encyclopedia of Plant Physiology, Vol. 12 (W. RUHLAND, ed.), Springer-Verlag, Berlin (1958a).
LUNDEGÅRDH, H. Physiol. Plant. **11**, 585 (1958b).

MACHLIS, L. J. Am. Jour. Botany 31, 183 (1944).
MARKS, J. D., BERNLOHR, R., and VARNER, J. E. Plant Physiol. 32, 259 (1957).
MARUO, B., AKAZAWA, T., and IIMURA, Y. Jour. Ag. Chem. Soc. Japan 27, 207 (1953).
MIDDLETON, L. J. Jour. Exp. Botany 6, 422 (1955).
MIDDLETON, L. J. New Phytol. 55, 117 (1956).
MILLER, G. W., and EVANS, H. J. Plant Physiol. 31, 357 (1956).
NEWCOMB, E. H., and STUMPF, P. K. Jour. Biol. Chem. 200, 233 (1955).
NIEDERGANG-KAMIEN, E., and LEOPOLD, A. C. Physiol. Plant. 10, 29 (1957).
ORDIN, L., and JACOBSON, L. Plant Physiol. 30, 21 (1955).
ÖSTERLIND, S. Physiol. Plant. 4, 528 (1951).
PENNELL, G. A., and WEATHERLEY, P. E. New Phytol. 57, 326 (1958).
POEL, L. W. Jour. Exp. Botany 4, 157 (1953).
PORTER, H. K., and RUNECKLES, S. V. C. Biochim. Biophys. Acta 20, 100 (1956).
REINHOLD, L. New Phytol. 53, 217 (1954).
ROBERTSON, R. N. Endeavour 16, 193 (1957).
ROBERTSON, R. N., in Encyclopedia of Plant Physiology, Vol. 4 (W. RUHLAND, ed.), Springer-Verlag, Berlin (1958).
ROBERTSON, R. N., and THORN, M. Australian Jour. Biol. Sci. 23, 305 (1945).
ROBERTSON, R. N., and TURNER, J. S. Australian Jour. Biol. Sci. 23, 63 (1945).
ROBERTSON, R. N., and WILKINS, M. J. Australian Jour. Sci. Res. 1, 17 (1948).
ROBERTSON, R. N., WILKINS, M. J., HOPE, A. B., and NESTEL, L. Australian Jour. Biol. Sci. 8, 164 (1955).
ROBERTSON, R. N., WILKINS, M. J., and WEEKS, D. C. Australian Jour. Sci. Res. 4, 248 (1951).
RUCKENBROD, H. Planta 46, 19 (1954).
SPENCER, M. S. Can. J. Biochem. Physiol. 37, 53 (1959).
STENLID, G. Physiol. Plant. 2, 61 (1949).
STEWARD, F. C. Protoplasma 15, 29 (1932).
STEWARD, F. C., and MILLAR, F. K. Soc. Exp. Biol. Symposia 8, 367 (1954).
STILLER, M. L. Ph.D. Thesis. Purdue University, Lafayette, Indiana (1959).
SUTCLIFFE, J. F., and HACKETT, D. P. Nature 180, 95 (1957).
ULRICH, A. Am. Jour. Botany 28, 526 (1941).
VAN LOOKEREN CAMPAGNE, R. N. Acta Botanica Neerland. 6, 543 (1957).
VENTURA, M. M. Rev. Brasil. Biol. 14, 153 (1954).
WEBSTER, G. C. Plant Physiol. 29, 202 (1954).
WEEKS, D. C., and ROBERTSON, R. N. Australian Jour. Sci. Res. 3, 487 (1950).
WILLENBRINK, J. Planta 48, 269 (1957).
YEMM, E. W., and WILLIS, A. J. New Phytol. 55, 229 (1956).

Chapter 9

Relationships

to Nitrogen Metabolism

The addition of nitrate or ammonium salts to suitable plant tissues brings about striking respiratory changes which probably include but go far beyond those induced by other salts discussed in the previous chapter (Willis and Yemm, 1955). It now appears that by providing a source of nitrogen which can be used in amino acid and protein synthesis a series of events is set in motion which has repercussions at many points in the respiratory mechanism (Figure 16).

Relationships between respiration and protein metabolism have been recognized for many years, and one interpretation of the available evidence, championed particularly by Steward, credits "alternating cycles of protein synthesis and breakdown with a major role in the path of carbon towards CO_2," (Steward and Pollard, 1957). Inherent in this view is the adoption of the so-called "alternate hypothesis" of protein production, in which the majority of the free amino acids are regarded primarily as products of protein breakdown rather than precursors in the synthesis. As Yemm and Folkes (1958) have pointed out, this interpretation of the available data is not the only one, and in an eloquent paper they have developed an over-all interpretation of relationships between respiration and protein metabolism which is in keeping with the more usual concept that free amino acids are precursors of proteins and with the pattern of respiratory control which has been outlined in an earlier chapter. In this limited discussion, then, we will adopt the prevailing (but not universal) view that, particularly in nonsenescent tissues, the breakdown of

177

carbohydrate to CO_2 does not include an excursion into nitrogenous compounds as in the protein cycle. We will indicate briefly what the current biochemical concepts on the steps in NO_3' utilization are and how these might conceivably affect respiration, and we will then examine the respiratory data to see how far these predictions are fulfilled.

a. *Uptake of nitrate.* The act of uptake of nitrate by plant tissues, particulary those low in salt but well supplied with carbohydrate, might itself lead to an increased rate of respiration (Chapter 8).

b. *Reduction of nitrate to ammonia by a series of 2-electron steps with suitable donors and reductases (Nason et al., 1954).* In higher plants the work by Evans', Nason's, and Nicholas' groups has established firmly that the steps in this sequence involve nitrate reductase (in which a flavin and molybdenum participate), nitrite reductase, and hydroxylamine reductase, with reduced nucleotides furnishing the reducing power (see Webster, 1959). Experiments which indicate that the PNH may derive more or less directly from the photolysis reaction in photosynthesis are discussed in Chapter 11. In nongreen cells and in all cells in the dark this reducing power (and ATP, if this is also required; see Kessler, 1955, 1957) must originate from respiratory oxidations, and we note that 4 moles of PNH would be required for the production of 1 mole of NH_3. The diversion of reduced nucleotides from normal electron-transfer sequences (with NO_3' substituting for O_2 as the electron acceptor) would be expected to reduce O_2 uptake without lowering CO_2 output; such is indeed the physiological finding (see below).

c. *Production of amino acids from NH_3.* Although the various keto acid analogues of the amino acids (Steward and Pollard, 1957) are potentially capable of reacting with ammonia to produce corresponding imino acids, the present indications are (Yemm and Folkes, 1958) that the primary port of entry into amino acids is by way of α-ketoglutarate, with subsequent transamination to other keto acid acceptors. The production of glutamic acid occurs via the corresponding imino acid, which is reduced by PNH in the presence of glutamic dehydrogenase. Whatever the final disposition of the question of primary incorporation may be, it is clear that for each amino acid which is produced a carbon skeleton is required and that a reductive amination must at some point have preceded the formation of each α-amino group. The possible repercussions on respiration are therefore twofold: a drainage of intermediates produced in respiratory carbohydrate breakdown (e.g., oxalacetic, α-ketoglutaric, and pyruvic acids) and a diversion of PNH.

d. *Incorporation of amino acids into proteins (and amides)*. We need not be concerned in the present context with the currently exciting problems of the mechanism of protein synthesis (see Webster, 1959). What seems to be established and germane is the requirement, as a prerequisite to incorporation or synthesis, of ATP, by which, in the presence of appropriate activating enzymes, the individual amino acids become converted into the corresponding adenylates. The utilization of a mole of ATP for each mole of amino acid converted to peptide (or amide) introduces a further vital connection to respiration. The increased turnover of ATP resulting from such a utilization would be expected to have, as a direct result, a stimulatory effect on respiration.

e. *Carbon skeletons from protein breakdown*. Finally it is recognized that in those tissues where protein breakdown predominates (Folkes and Yemm, 1958), e.g., some germinating seeds and senescent leaves, a partial reversal of this drain on respiration may occur. This is to say, some of the carbon skeletons from the deaminated products of protein hydrolysis (and the resulting PNH) might be returned to the milieu of respiratory intermediates and be further degraded in energy-yielding reactions, thus sparing the available carbohydrate reserves or perhaps even replacing them entirely.

The experiments of Yemm's group are particularly pertinent to this discussion since they have provided the best evidence we have for the operation *in vivo* of the above-mentioned effects in higher plants. An important investigation of similar problems in *Chlorella* is that of Syrett (1953, 1956a,b). When nitrate or ammonia is added to excised barley roots, it

TABLE XXXII

CARBON BALANCE SHEET FOR BARLEY ROOTS DURING THE ASSIMILATION OF 0.0025 M AMMONIUM PHOSPHATE, SODIUM NITRATE, AND NITRITE* (YEMM AND WILLIS, 1956)

N Source	$NH_4H_2PO_4$			$NaNO_3$		$NaNO_2$	
Assimilation Period (Hr.)	9½	18½	27½	9½	18½	9½	18½
(1) Lost as CO_2	19.7	36.6	49.9	21.8	40.5	22.2	45.0
(2) Synthesis of glutamine	11.3	15.9	15.9	0.9	0.8	1.9	4.4
(3) Synthesis of asparagine	0.5	2.8	4.8	0.3	1.1	0.3	0.7
(4) Total of (1), (2), and (3)	31.5	55.3	70.6	23.0	42.4	24.4	50.1
(5) Lost from sugars	42.8	61.7	76.5	20.3	50.3	20.4	46.2
(6) Difference [(5) − (4)]	11.3	6.4	5.9	5.3	7.9	−4.0	−3.9

*The results are expressed as mg. C/100 root systems.

is rapidly incorporated into organic nitrogen compounds; the primary products are glutamine and glutamic, aspartic, and other amino acids (Yemm and Willis, 1956). From experiments in which nitrate and nitrite were compared as N sources it became clear that nitrite was the more rapidly consumed; in contrast to nitrate, it never accumulated in more than trace amounts in the tissue. The production of N compounds was accompanied by an increased breakdown of carbohydrate (Table XXXII), and the extent of this breakdown was sufficient to account for the C skeleton (section c, above) and for the extra CO_2 produced when the N source was supplied (see also Hamner, 1936).

The increased intensity of respiration—amounting to an 80–100% increase in CO_2 output—was a very striking feature of the behavior of the roots in response to nitrate, nitrite, or ammonia. We may note in regard to section a, above, that this stimulation was very much greater than that induced by other salts and that it occurred in spite of the fact that breakdown products of sugar were being actively consumed in the synthesis of glutamic acid and glutamine. It is important in view of section b, above, that the O_2 uptake was not stimulated to an equal degree by the various forms of N; the respiratory quotients are in fact quite revealing (Figure 23). Thus in the presence of nitrite, which is rapidly utilized, the R.Q. was

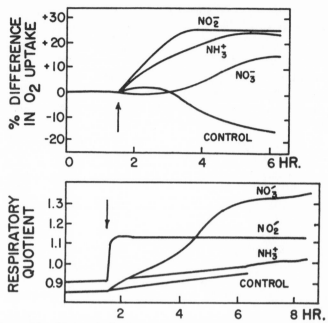

FIGURE 23.—Changes in O_2 absorption and R. Q. on adding various N sources to barley roots. Additions made at $1\frac{1}{2}$ hr. as follows: NO_2', sodium nitrite 0.005 M; NO_3', sodium nitrate 0.025 M; NH_3^+, ammonium phosphate 0.025 M. (After Willis and Yemm, 1955.)

immediately raised from the control level of 0.85 to 1.1 and was maintained for several hours. When nitrate was provided, the R.Q. began to rise strikingly after two hours and had reached 1.4 a few hours later. "Nitrate respiration" was first described by Warburg and Negelein (1920) working with *Chlorella,* and in Syrett's (1956a) experiments with this organism the R.Q. rose as high as 2.5 when nitrate was supplied. These observations may be accounted for (Willis and Yemm, 1955) by supposing that a fraction of the electron flux which would normally have passed to O_2 (with concomitant ATP production) was diverted and used instead in the reductive events accompanying the incorporation of nitrate and nitrite into organic forms of N (see also Ducet and Hewitt, 1954). Nitrate and nitrite can be viewed as substitutes for O_2 as the final electron acceptor, and the R.Q. would be increased from unity according to how big a fraction of the electron flux was diverted. It is most significant that, by contrast, the utilization of ammonia was not accompanied by any change in the R.Q., although the respiratory rate was strikingly stimulated (Figure 23). Some recent experiments have indicated that the utilization of nitrite induces a qualitative change in the respiratory pattern in root tips of maize. These results are thought to be due to the provision of reducing power (TPNH) by the pentose phosphate sequence, whose participation is induced by various agents which can reoxidize TPNH (Butt and Beevers, 1960).

Good evidence that prior to the addition of the nitrogen salts the ATP turnover in the barley roots was low is supplied by the striking response to DNP (Yemm and Willis, 1956). The over-all increase in respiratory rate when N is supplied can be reasonably ascribed to an increased availability of ADP (sections c and d, above). Some analogous experiments with yeast by Yemm and Folkes (1953, 1954) provided extensive data to support this view. In the absence of NH_3 the respiration and the (measured) loss of carbohydrate rose strikingly as the concentration of DNP around the cells was increased. The levels reached were about the same as those which were arrived at by the addition of NH_3 by itself; the addition of DNP had no additional effect in the presence of NH_3 (see also Syrett's [1958] experiments with *Chlorella*). As Folkes and Yemm (1958) point out, protein synthesis is but an example, though an outstanding one, of the closely co-ordinated endergonic processes which constitute growth and which contribute to the regulation of the metabolic rate through their demands for energy and metabolites.

Additional evidence for the origin of the C skeletons comes from many experiments in which C^{14}-labeled sugars have been provided to plant tissues. Steward, Bidwell, and Yemm (1958) emphasized the very active incorporation of carbon from glucose-U-C^{14} into amide and protein fractions in their experiments with carrots. Acetate has been shown to furnish carbon which entered amino acid and protein pools in growing wheat plants (McConnell and Mazurek, 1956) and in leaves (Rogers, 1955; McConnell and Ramachandran, 1956; Bilinski and McConnell, 1957a,b, 1958b). The production of amino acids and subsequently protein was shown to be a feature of pyruvate utilization in growing tissues (Bilinski and McConnell, 1958a; McConnell *et al.*, 1960; Neal and Beevers, 1960).

In view of the close association of amino acid synthesis with respiration that is indicated by the experiments *in vivo*, it is of interest that glutamic dehydrogenase and various transaminases have been shown to be present on mitochondria, where some of the important keto acids originate (Chapter 6). We may note, too, that amide synthesis may also occur on these organelles (Webster, 1959). Presumably this association is of some functional value when amino acids are being utilized as an energy source, as during germination of seeds rich in protein (Folkes and Yemm, 1958). The oxidation of a number of amino acids by mitochondria from etiolated seedlings of *Avena sterilis* was demonstrated by Rautenen and Tager (1955) and by Smillie (1955) in pea-leaf mitochondria. Glutamate oxidation and coupled phosphorylation have been observed by a number of authors.

REFERENCES

BILINSKI, E., and McCONNELL, W. B. Can. J. Biochem. Physiol. 35, 365 (1957a).
BILINSKI, E., and McCONNELL, W. B. Can. J. Biochem. Physiol. 35, 357 (1957b).
BILINSKI, E., and McCONNELL, W. B. Cereal Chem. 35, 66 (1958a).
BILINSKI, E., and McCONNELL, W. B. Can. J. Biochem. Physiol. 36, 381 (1958b).
BUTT, V. S., and BEEVERS, H. Biochem. Jour. 76, 51P (1960).
DUCET, G., and HEWITT, E. J. Nature 173, 1141 (1954).
FOLKES, B. F., and YEMM, E. W. New Phytol. 57, 106 (1958).
HAMNER, K. C. Bot. Gaz. 97, 744 (1936).
KESSLER, E. Planta 45, 94 (1955).
KESSLER, E. Planta 49, 505 (1957).
McCONNELL, W. G., and MAZUREK, T. Biochim. Biophys. Acta 21, 183 (1956).
McCONNELL, W. B., and RAMACHANDRAN, L. K. Can. J. Biochem. Physiol. 38, 33 (1960).
NASON, A., ABRAHAM, R. G., and AUERBACH, B. L. Biochim. Biophys. Acta 15, 159 (1954).
NEAL, G. E., and BEEVERS, H. Biochem. Jour. 74, 409 (1960).
RAUTENEN, N., and TAGER, J. M. Ann. Acad. Sci. Fennicae (Ser. A) 60, 241 (1955).

ROGERS, B. J. Plant Physiol. **30**, 377 (1955).
SMILLIE, R. M. Australian Jour. Sci. **17**, 217 (1955).
STEWARD, F. C., and POLLARD, J. K. Ann. Rev. Plant Physiol. **8**, 65 (1957).
STEWARD, F. C., BIDWELL, R. G. S., and YEMM, E. W. Jour. Exp. Botany **9**, 11 (1958).
SYRETT, P. J. Ann. Botany (N.S.) **17**, 1 (1953).
SYRETT, P. J. Physiol. Plant. **9**, 19 (1956a).
SYRETT, P. J. Physiol. Plant. **9**, 28 (1956b).
SYRETT, P. J. Arch. Biochem. Biophys. **75**, 117 (1958).
WARBURG, O., and NEGELEIN, E. Biochem. Zeitschr. **110**, 66 (1920).
WEBSTER, G. C. *Nitrogen Metabolism in Plants*, Row, Peterson, Evanston, Ill. (1959).
WILLIS, A. J., and YEMM, E. W. New Phytol. **54**, 163 (1955).
YEMM, E. W., and FOLKES, B. F. Biochem. Jour. **55**, 700 (1953).
YEMM, E. W., and FOLKES, B. F. Biochem. Jour. **57**, 495 (1954).
YEMM, E. W., and FOLKES, B. F. Ann. Rev. Plant Physiol. **9**, 245 (1958).
YEMM, E. W., and WILLIS, A. J. New Phytol. **55**, 229 (1956).

Chapter 10

Relationships to Growth

O_2 is required for the growth of higher plants, and the synthesis of complex cellular materials from simple precursors must be accompanied by some exergonic reaction. These facts have encouraged the view, long held, that energy released in aerobic respiration is the driving force. As a result of research on plant metabolism during the past ten years, this conviction has become a reality. The demonstration that ATP is a tangible and useful product of respiratory oxidations in plants (Chapter 5) was the first step. The second step in establishing this link was the recognition that in a variety of synthetic events essential to growth—amide and peptide synthesis, polysaccharide and fat synthesis may be quoted as examples—ATP was specifically required. The striking inhibitory effects on growth of the uncoupling agents such as DNP (Bonner, 1949a,b; French and Beevers, 1953) become understandable on this basis. It should be emphasized that it is not the heat generated by a simple hydrolysis of ATP which drives these various reactions; ATP is required in stoichiometric amounts to convert the precursors into more reactive forms which are the substrates for subsequent enzyme-catalyzed steps. In some instances these forms are phosphorylated derivatives, e.g., hexose phosphates; in others, the adenylate moiety itself becomes attached, e.g., in acetate and amino acid activation.

This link with respiration, though important, is not of course the only one. In a variety of reactions essential to growth, e.g., reductive amination of α-keto acids, fat synthesis, and NO_3' and SO_4'' reduction, reduced nucleotides are specifically required. The diversion of these nucleotides, generated in respiration, from the usual oxidative pathways has repercussions on the O_2 uptake (Kandler, 1950; Willis and Yemm, 1955) and even on the pathways of glucose utilization (Butt and Beevers, 1960). Further, the diversion of respiratory intermediates to posts as tissue constituents, which had appeared likely for many years, now has some solid evidence from tracer experiments with sugars and pyruvate to support it (Figure 24). The extent of this diversion is just now becoming recognized; we may note in passing that it has im-

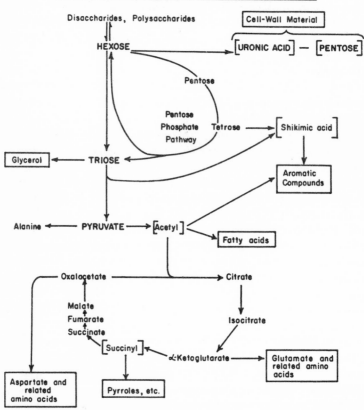

FIGURE 24.—Diagram to show some of the points at which respiratory intermediates might be diverted in synthetic events.

portant repercussions on the relative contributions of the individual carbons of glucose to the respired CO_2.

From the foregoing considerations it might be deduced that under conditions of rapid synthesis and growth respiration rates would be increased. The mechanism whereby a rather precise regulation of respiration may be imposed by such events has been dealt with earlier (Chapter 7). Data are now available on the respiration of plant parts of different ages (see Dittmer and Grebe, 1958, for a massive compilation). It is clear that the highest Q_{O2} values (on a weight-of-tissue basis) are typically found in meristematic regions, where cells are small and nonvacuolated, and the lowest in those organs which have ceased active growth. Similar conclusions have been reached from experiments in which growing and nongrowing cells of the same tissue are compared (Rabideau and Whaley, 1950; Steward and Bidwell, 1958). Considerable stress has been laid on the rate of respiration/unit protein, and the constancy of this value under some conditions has led some authors to conclude that respiration and protein metabolism are inextricably connected (Gregory and Sen, 1937; Chibnall, 1939; Steward and Pollard, 1957). However, *inter alia*, Jensen (1955) has observed that there may be several-fold changes in the values for respiration rate/unit protein/cell within very short distances along a bean root tip, and Pearson and Robertson (1953) showed that the roughly constant relationship between respiratory rate and protein content of apple fruits broke down during the climacteric. Yemm and Folkes (1958), in a recent and valuable review, have given good reasons for supposing that the rate of protein synthesis is more important in determining rates of respiration than is protein content. James (1953, p. 19) has emphasized that insofar as protein synthesis may include the formation of "catalytic protoplasm" the capacity of respiration will increase during cellular growth. The work of Lund, Vatter, and Hanson (1958) on elongating corn roots leaves no doubt that striking increases in mitochondrial bulk occur as a meristematic root-tip cell progresses toward a fully elongated one (see also Whaley *et al.*, 1959). Similar striking increases occur during

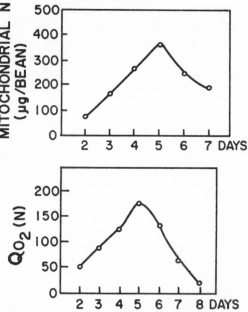

FIGURE 25.—Changes in *(upper graph)* the amount of mitochondrial N in the endosperm and *(lower graph)* the specific ability of the mitochondria to oxidize α-ketoglutarate during germination of castor beans. (Akazawa and Beevers, 1957.)

germination (Figure 25). At the same time as the mitochondrial protein increases, its specific respiratory capacity also increases, and Lund *et al.* (1958) consider that in their material this may be related to the observed extensive development of cristae within the mitochondria themselves (see also Palade, 1956).

In attempting to define the relationship between growth and respiration, the unit of choice is not the whole plant or organ, although these pose interesting problems (Briggs *et al.*, 1921), but the individual cell (see Loewenberg, 1955). Successful measurements of respiration on small samples of tissue comprising known numbers of more or less similar cells have been made from several organs in the past ten years. We may note, as pointed out by Loewenberg (1955), that the values available for respiration rate/cell, shown in Table XXXIII, fall into a relatively narrow range, in which the maximum variation is about tenfold. The variation in cell weight or size may be considerably more extreme than this; it amounts in the apple, for example, to two-hundred-fold.

Brown and his colleagues have measured respiratory and other characteristics of sections 0.2–0.6 mm. thick cut serially along growing tips of pea roots, and Jensen working with roots of the broad bean has concentrated on the first three millimeters, using selected 0.2-mm. sections for analysis (Table XXXIV). It should be emphasized that these sections are much smaller than those used in earlier work, which estab-

TABLE XXXIII
RESPIRATORY RATES OF PLANT CELLS

Tissue	Respiration Rate; CO_2 Output $(mg \times 10^{-8}\ CO_2$ Hour/Cell)	Authors
Apple fruit	1.3–17	Pearson and Robertson (1953)
Bean root tip	1.3–7.8	Jensen (1955)
Corn root tip	1.8–9.6	Goddard, cited by Loewenberg (1955)
Onion root tip	1.2–10	Wanner (1950)
Pea root tip	2 –12	Brown and Broadbent (1950)
Maturing pea seed	3.3–16	McKee Robertson, and Lee (1955)
Maturing bean seed	1.4–18	Loewenberg (1955)

TABLE XXXIV
RESPIRATION RATES IN BEAN ROOT TIPS (JENSEN, 1955)

DISTANCE FROM TIP	O_2 UPTAKE PER HOUR		
	Per Section (0.2 mm Thick)	Per Cell	Per $m\mu g$ Protein N/Cell
0–0.4 mm (Root cap)	$3.39 \times 10^{-3}\ \mu l$	$29.4 \times 10^{-6}\ \mu l$	$589 \times 10^{-6}\ \mu l$
0.4–0.5 mm	6.0	6.3	140
1.2 mm	11.75	9.2	61
1.8 mm	38.19	25.7	135
2.0 mm	49.20	32.4	202
3.0 mm	54.10	37.0	282

lished that successive 10-mm. sections along a root axis showed sharply decreasing respiratory rates. Thus all of the cells which have now been examined in detail by Jensen and by Brown were included in the first segment in the earlier work (see, e.g., Machlis, 1944). Some very important changes occur in the first few millimeters of the root, to which cell division and enlargement are largely confined.

It has become clear that at the tip proper (i.e., excluding the root cap) the respiration rate/segment is very low and rises strikingly to a peak, which in the broad bean appears to be at about 3 mm. and in pea at 1.3 mm. From this peak the rate declines along the axis, as found in the earlier work. Of greater importance is the finding that the respiration rate per cell also increases strikingly in passing from a region in which cell division predominates to one of enlargement (Table XXXIV). The highest respiration rates are not found in the meristematic zone; on the contrary, these cells are characterized by low rates on whatever basis these are expressed (see also Goddard and Meeuse, 1950, and references therein).

It is tempting to think that during this and immediately subsequent stages catalytic protein is being built up and that the rate of ATP turnover is sufficiently high to keep the existing respiratory machinery operating at full capacity. Certainly the stimulation induced by DNP is minimal in the youngest tissues which have been examined (Beevers, 1953; Gaur and Beevers, 1957; Eliasson and Mathiesen, 1956). Control by a diminishing rate of ATP turnover apparently becomes impressed only in considerably older cells than those used by Brown and by Jensen. Eliasson and Mathiesen observed maximal stimulation by DNP in cells 4–5 cm. from the apex, and in comparable experiments with coleoptiles and hypocotyls by Gaur and Beevers a similar conclusion was reached.

The aspect of plant growth which has been most intensively studied in relation to respiration is that of cells of coleoptiles, pea internodes, or storage tissue undergoing vacuolation and expansion. One of the attractive features of such material is that the growth can be elicited by the application of suitable concentrations of growth-regulating substances such as indoleacetic acid. The most striking feature of coleoptile growth is the increase in the volume of the cell and of the cell-wall material surrounding it. Some net protein synthesis also occurs during this time (Thimann, 1951; Thimann and Loos, 1957). The close relationship of growth to respiration has been amply established with such material (see Bonner, 1949a,b; Thimann, 1951). A large number of treatments which interfere with respiration—e.g., inhibitors of glycolysis, the TCA cycle, or electron transfer, and withholding O_2—also slow down growth to at least an equal degree. The finding that, under appropriate conditions, growth may be completely (but light-reversibly) inhibited by CO (Thimann *et al.*, 1954; Hackett *et al.*, 1953a,b) at levels which did not completely stop O_2 uptake has emphasized the indispensability of the cytochrome system to this aspect of cellular work. Such demonstrations have given rise to the view, arrived at also from other experiments (e.g., those on salt uptake, Chapter 8), that a fraction of the respiration—basal respiration—is incapable of supporting work and is perhaps accommodated by different oxidases, while the respiratory increases elicited by stimulants such as salts and growth regulators (and, it should be noted, by DNP) are completely wiped out by inhibitors of the cytochrome oxidase. This recalls the view that a fraction of the respiration is required for maintenance and that only when a certain rate of respiration is exceeded is energy channeled into growth (see, e.g., Plantefoil and Moyse, 1953). Direct and unequivocal demonstration of this is not at present available.

An important observation which has frequently been repeated is that cells capable of showing a positive growth response when IAA is added also show an increased respiration which is usually 115–130% of the control rate. (Inhibitory effects of growth regulators need not concern us here.) This finding encouraged speculation that these compounds are active because they directly accelerate some part of the respiratory machinery. Exhaustive searches for stimulatory effects on respiratory enzymes have not met with success. At one time several authorities (Bonner et al., 1953; Thimann, 1951) thought it likely that auxin-induced metabolic water uptake might be an important aspect of cell expansion, and a proposal was made that IAA "channels the energy of ATP into the performance of water accumulation work" (Bonner et al., 1953). The stimulated respiration would thus follow inevitably from the resulting increased turnover of ATP (see also Bonner and Bandurski, 1952). The view that IAA acts by directly influencing water uptake is no longer widely held nor is it indeed tenable (Levitt, 1953; Burstrom, 1953; Kettellapper, 1953; Ordin, Applewhite, and Bonner, 1956), but the concept that the stimulated respiration is due to an increased turnover of ATP remains a valuable one (see also French and Beevers, 1953).

The prevailing view now is that the primary effect of IAA must be on some aspect of cell-wall metabolism and synthesis (Kettellapper, 1953). The resulting increase in area of the cell wall would relax to some extent the inward pressure of the wall and thus increase the suction pressure (diffusion pressure deficit). Water movement into the cell by osmosis would follow and cell expansion would result. Without in any way explaining the precise action of IAA, this interpretation is in keeping with that we know about cell-wall synthesis and would assign a similar mechanism for the respiratory rise to that which results from the performance of other kinds of cellular work.

While this much is generally agreed (but see Marrè, Forti, and Gaur, 1960), there is considerable disagreement as to when the increased formation of new cell-wall material occurs in relation to the respiratory rise and as to whether all of the increase in respiration is to be ascribed to this cause. Recent work on the early stages of the cell's response to IAA has revealed that the primary step may be a loosening or plasticizing of the existing cell-wall material (Kettellapper, 1953; Busse and Kandler, 1956; Cleland and Bonner, 1956). Busse and Kandler suggest that increased respiration is not associated with this first phase but becomes evident only later as a result of deposition of new material in the cell wall (with a consequently increased ATP turnover) after the cell has begun enlargement. Cleland and Bonner (1956) showed that the events in this early phase, which can be neatly separated from succeeding ones by the use of isotonic media, were strictly aerobic and sensitive to DNP, but Busse and Kandler do not find the immediate respiratory rise on adding IAA which might have been expected and which others have described (Bonner et al., 1953; French and Beevers, 1953). They therefore question the rigidity of the relationship between growth and respiration in their immediate responses to IAA. Marrè and his colleagues (Marrè and Arrigoni, 1957; Marrè and Forti, 1958) have also had cause to question whether the immediate effect of IAA was one of increased ATP turnover. They have found in fact that the ATP/ADP ratio in pea-stem sections actually increased during the first 30 minutes in contact with IAA, and they attach importance to the fact that effects are noted on the levels of oxidized and reduced glutathione. Furthermore, these authors showed that it is possible under some circumstances to increase the respiration in response to DNP still further by IAA addition, and similar results have been obtained by Newcomb (1955) and Reinhold (1956). Such a result is not anticipated from the earlier work. We may conclude that the details of the relationships between IAA-induced growth and respiration are not finally established and will probably have to await the solution of the problem of the primary action of the growth regulator.

Although the problem of energy sources for growth has been extensively studied in microorganisms (for a review see Clifton, 1946), there is surprisingly little information on the important question of how efficiently respiration may be geared to growth in higher plant cells. Carbohydrate can be regarded as the starting point for both, and the relative amounts of substrate respired and converted into more permanent cellular materials may be evaluated. Goddard (1948) quotes some experiments of Meeuse on developing pea embryos from which it was calculated that roughly 60% of the glucose was respired while 40% was used in synthetic events. Kandler (1953), in an important study, evaluated the "synthetischer Wirkungsgrad," a ratio showing the relative amounts of sugar assimilated and respired in maize embryos growing in tissue culture. All of the parts studied gave evidence of a considerable diversion of sugars to products of growth; the maximum efficiency was observed in the 5-day embryo, in which almost 2 moles of glucose were assimilated for each mole respired. Tang *et al.* (1959) have demonstrated that in rice seedlings the synthetic efficiency is about 50%; for each unit of dry matter lost as CO_2 from the seedling a unit of embryo dry weight was produced.

It would be valuable to know in more detail just how much oxidative assimilation occurs in widely different types of tissues and which of the intermediate products of carbohydrate breakdown are diverted. The information in hand about pathways of synthesis of some components, e.g., protein and fat precursors, indicates some of the important drainage points (Figure 24). Recent work has also given firm indications of the pathways of synthesis of cell-wall constituents (see Gibbs, 1959). By the elegant use of tracer methods Neish and his group (Neish, 1955, 1958; Altermatt and Neish, 1956) have arrived at probable reaction sequences in the production and incorporation into cellulose and hemicellulose of hexose, hexuronic acid, and pentose residues. Hassid's group has also contributed substantially to this understanding, particularly by demonstrating that uridine diphospho-derivatives of the hexose and other intermediates are present and that enzyme systems capable of bringing about some of the key reactions are available (Hassid, Neufeld, and Feingold, 1959). In addition to the drainage of hexose units, the participation of a reaction involving decarboxylation of uridine diphosphoglucuronic acid at C-6 should be noted, since it has repercussions on the contribution of individual carbons to respired CO_2 (Slater and Beevers, 1958; Butt and Beevers, 1960).

Progress has also been made, particularly by Neish's group, in the origin of aromatic compounds, flavonols, and lignin precursors, in which the formation of shikimic acid is an important first step (see reviews by Bogorad, 1959, and Neish, 1960). Drainage of tetrose and 3-C intermediates for this synthesis would represent an important feature of glucose dissimilation in some cells. The use of acetate as a precursor of some cyclic components should not be overlooked (Watkin, Underhill, and Neish, 1957).

The occurrence of these and other synthetic events would be expected, first, to result in a diversion of glucose; but according to what materials were being synthesized, different intermediates would be drawn off, and thus the fates of the individual glucose carbons would be different. We can already deduce from experiments with specifically labeled glucose and other compounds (pyruvate, acetate) that the individual carbons contribute in different measure to the respired CO_2 and to the permanent structural materials. The respired CO_2 is found frequently to be made up largely of carbons from positions 1, 3, and 4 of the glucose, while the bulk of carbons 2, 5, and 6 may be incorporated into cellular products (Barbour et al., 1958; Doyle and Wang, 1958; ap Rees and Beevers, 1960).

These results indicate that the major points of drainage for synthesis (in addition to those in which diversion of more or less intact hexose residues into cell-wall components occurs) involve acetate units and the TCA cycle. Experiments with labeled acetate and pyruvate (Chapter 3) also give clear evidence of such diversion. Recent work in which the fates of individual carbons of pyruvate have been followed quantitatively has indicated the extent of this diversion in different types of tissue. The most effective use of pyruvate for synthetic events was in the growing corn mesocotyl, in which 45% of the added pyruvate (from C-2 and C-3 only) was retained in the tissue, much of it in protein. In a nongrowing tissue, mature petiole, there was virtually no retention (Neal and Beevers, 1960).

REFERENCES

ALTERMATT, H. A., and NEISH, A. C. Can. J. Biochem. Physiol. 34, 405 (1956).
AKAZAWA, T., and BEEVERS, H. Biochem. Jour. 67, 115 (1957).
AP REES, T., and BEEVERS, H. Plant Physiol. 35, 839 (1960).
BARBOUR, R. D., BUHLER, D. R., and WANG, C. H. Plant Physiol. 33, 396 (1958).
BEEVERS, H. Am. Jour. Botany 40, 91 (1953).

BOGORAD, L. Ann. Rev. Plant Physiol. **9,** 417 (1959).
BONNER, J. Am. Jour. Botany **36,** 323 (1949a).
BONNER, J. Am. Jour. Botany **36,** 429 (1949b).
BONNER, J., and BANDURSKI, R. S. Ann. Rev. Plant Physiol. **3,** 59 (1952).
BONNER, J., BANDURSKI, R. S., and MILLERD, A. Physiol. Plant. **6,** 511 (1953).
BRIGGS, G. E., KIDD, F. L., and WEST, C. Ann. Applied Biol. **7,** 103 (1921).
BROWN, R., and BROADBENT, D. Jour. Exp. Botany **1,** 249 (1950).
BROWN, R., REITH, W. S., and ROBINSON, E. Symp. Soc. Exp. Biol. **6,** 329 (1952).
BURSTROM, H. Physiol. Plant. **6,** 262 (1953).
BUSSE, M., and KANDLER, O. Planta **46,** 619 (1956).
BUTT, V. S., and BEEVERS, H. Biochem. Jour. **76,** 51P (1960).
CHIBNALL, A. C. *Protein Metabolism in the Plant,* Yale University Press, New Haven (1939).
CLELAND, R., and BONNER, J. Plant Physiol. **31,** 350 (1956).
CLIFTON, C. E. Adv. Enzymol. **6,** 269 (1946).
DITTMER, D. S., and GREBE, R. M. (eds.) *Handbook of Respiration* (WADC Technical Report 58-352), U.S. Air Force (1958).
DOYLE, W. P., and WANG, C. H. Can. J. Botany **36,** 483 (1958).
ELIASSON, L., and MATHIESEN, I. Physiol. Plant. **9,** 265 (1956).
FRENCH, R. C., and BEEVERS, H. Am. Jour. Botany **40,** 660 (1953).
GAUR, B. K., and BEEVERS, H. Unpublished data (1957).
GIBBS, M. Ann. Rev. Plant Physiol. **10,** 329 (1959).
GODDARD, D. R. Growth **12,** 17 (1948).
GODDARD, D. R., and MEEUSE, B. J. D. Ann. Rev. Plant Physiol. **1,** 207 (1950).
GREGORY, F. G., and SEN, P. K. Ann. Botany (N.S.) **1,** 521 (1937).
HACKETT, D. P., and SCHNEIDERMAN, H. A. Arch. Biochem. Biophys. **47,** 190 (1953a).
HACKETT, D. P., SCHNEIDERMAN, H. A., and THIMANN, K. V. Arch. Biochem. Biophys. **47,** 205 (1953b).
HASSID, W. Z., NEUFELD, E. F., and FEINGOLD, D. S. Proc. Nat. Acad. Sci. **45,** 1 (1959).
JAMES, W. O. *Plant Respiration,* Clarendon Press, Oxford (1953).
JENSEN, W. A. Exp. Cell Res. **8,** 506 (1955).
KANDLER, O. Z. Naturforsch. **5(b),** 203 (1950).
KANDLER, O. Z. Naturforsch. **8(b),** 105 (1953).
KETTELLAPPER, H. J. Acta Botanica Neerland. **2,** 387 (1953).
LEVITT, J. Physiol. Plant. **6,** 240 (1953).
LOEWENBERG, J. R. Plant Physiol. **30,** 244 (1955).
LUND, H. A., VATTER, A. E., and HANSON, J. B. Jour. Biophys. Biochem. Cytol. **4,** 87 (1958).
MACHLIS, L. J. Am. Jour. Botany **31,** 281 (1944).
MARRÈ, E., and ARRIGONI, O. Physiol. Plant. **10,** 289 (1957).
MARRÈ, E., and FORTI, G. Physiol. Plant. **11,** 36 (1958).
MARRÈ, E., FORTI, G., and GAUR, B. K. Plant Physiol. **35,** 45 (1960).
MCKEE, H. S., ROBERTSON, R. H., and LEE, J. B. Australian Jour. Biol. Sci. **8,** 137 (1955).
NEAL, G. E., and BEEVERS, H. Biochem. Jour. **74,** 409 (1960).
NEISH, A. C. Can. J. Biochem. Physiol. **33,** 658 (1955).
NEISH, A. C. Can. J. Biochem. Physiol. **36,** 187 (1958).
NEISH, A. C. Ann. Rev. Plant Physiol. **11,** 55 (1960).
NEWCOMB, E. H. Ann. Biol. **59,** 195 (1955).

ORDIN, L., APPLEWHITE, T. H., and BONNER, J. Plant Physiol. 31, 44 (1956).

PALADE, G. E., in *Enzymes: Units of Biological Structure and Function* (O. H. GAEBLER, ed.), Academic Press, New York (1956).

PEARSON, J. A., and ROBERTSON, R. N. Australian Jour. Sci. Res. B6, 1 (1953).

PLANTEFOIL, L., and MOYSE, A. Proc. Inter. Bot. Congress (Stockholm) 7, 761 (1953).

RABIDEAU, G. S., and WHALEY, W. G. Plant Physiol. 25, 334 (1950).

REINHOLD, L. Personal communication (1956).

SLATER, W. G., and BEEVERS, H. Plant Physiol. 33, 146 (1958).

STEWARD, F. C., and POLLARD, J. K. Ann. Rev. Plant Physiol. 8, 65 (1957).

STEWARD, F. C., and BIDWELL, R. G. S. Jour. Exp. Botany 9, 285 (1958).

TANG, P. S., WANG, F. C., and CHIH, F. C. Scientia Sinica 8 (11), 1379 (1959).

THIMANN, K. V. Growth 15, 5 (1951).

THIMANN, K. V., YOCUM, C. S., and HACKETT, D. P. Arch. Biochem. Biophys. 53, 239 (1954).

THIMANN, K. V., and LOOS, G. M. Plant Physiol. 32, 274 (1957).

WANNER, H. Rev. schweiz. bot. Ges. 60, 404 (1950).

WATKIN, J. E., UNDERHILL, E. W., and NEISH, A. C. Can. J. Biochem. Physiol. 35, 229 (1957).

WHALEY, W. G., KEPHART, J. E., and MOLLENHAUER, H. H. Am. Jour. Botany 46, 743 (1959).

WILLIS, A. J., and YEMM, E. W. New Phytol. 54, 163 (1955).

YEMM, E. W., and FOLKES, B. F. Ann. Rev. Plant Physiol. 9, 245 (1958).

Chapter 11

Relationships

to Photosynthesis

The most obvious relationships between respiration and photosynthesis are those shown by the over-all equations. The starting materials for one process are the end products of the other. The recognition of this relationship is implicit in the corrections for respiration during measurements of photosynthesis, the need for studying respiration of green tissue (by conventional methods) in the dark, and the concept of the compensation point. At one time photosynthesis and respiration were thought to be completely separate processes, and it was considered just an unfortunate circumstance, making measurements less precise, that the two processes should be reciprocally related in this way. Nothing was implied or deduced about possible connections or parallel mechanisms until quite recently.

Now that the biochemistry of the two processes has been outlined, it is clear that the relationships may be a great deal more intimate than is revealed by the equations. Some enzymes and intermediates are common to both sequences, and there are several points of contact and possible interchange. It should be emphasized at the outset, however, that at the same time as the possibility of biochemical interrelations has been increased by the accumulated information, parallel work on biochemical topography has afforded additional reasons for retaining the notion of separateness.

Thus the burden of a good deal of Arnon's recent work (e.g., Arnon, 1955) has been the self-sufficiency of the chloroplast as a photosynthetic unit. It now seems clear that co-operation with cytoplasmic enzymes is not necessary for carbohydrate production and that losses of individual enzymes during separation may account for the fact that the isolated chloroplasts have only a fraction of the photosynthetic activity of the parent tissue. Similarly, the mitochondria have become, for most authors, the exclusive site of pyruvate oxidation and oxidative phosphorylation, while the enzymes for the initial stage of glucose breakdown occur outside these organelles (see Chapter 6). As a result, the participation of glycolytic intermediates and enzymes, the pyridine nucleotide coenzymes, and the adenylates in both processes does not mean that they are acting in common pools and that all of the possibilities of interaction are in fact realized. It now appears that in order to account for some of the interactions described below we must assume that some traffic occurs between the organelles *in vivo*, but at present there is no direct evidence on this question. We will not be concerned in this discussion with the exit from the chloroplast of the finished photosynthetic product, which is, of course, the starting point for the bulk of the respiration in the plant generally. Figure 26 expresses in a simplified way the possible bearing of each process on the other; the involvement of common intermediates, coenzymes, and adenylates is of particular interest here.

Franck (1953), in an important article, gave good reasons for invoking the contribution of respiratory intermediates (generated, one would suppose, outside the chloroplasts) to carbohydrate production under certain conditions. The conditions under which a high influx of respiratory intermediates might be expected are just those which are required for the observation of "abnormally high" quantum efficiencies of photosynthesis (i.e., low light intensity for brief periods). Bassham *et al.* (1955) contribute to this view in explaining their results on the relationship between light at low intensity and quantum efficiency. Observations on the production of carbohydrate from intermediates such as alanine (Burma and Mortimer, 1957) and organic acids in the light (Burris, 1953) are also important here.

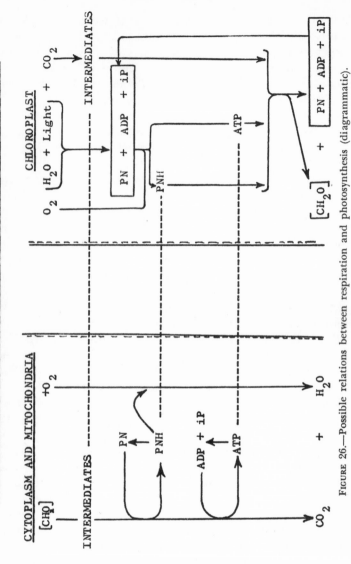

FIGURE 26.—Possible relations between respiration and photosynthesis (diagrammatic).

Evidence for the converse effect, i.e., a movement of "photosynthetic" intermediates into "respiratory" sequences, is found in the fact that compounds related to the TCA cycle are among early products in the light. There is some evidence, however, that only a limited amount of carbon from phosphoglyceric acid passes to pyruvate and so to the TCA cycle when photosynthesis is proceeding. Certainly, when the light is removed, there is a surge of newly acquired carbon into the TCA-cycle intermediates (Calvin and Massini, 1952; Gibbs, 1953; Bassham *et al.*, 1956). However, this cannot be ascribed to the blocking of the TCA apparatus in the presence of light because exogenously supplied intermediates such as pyruvate (Milhaud *et al.*, 1956) and glutamate (Naylor and Tolbert, 1956; Bidwell *et al.*, 1955) can be rapidly utilized. It seems more likely that the failure of more of the newly acquired carbon (but perhaps not that of compounds outside the chloroplasts) to enter the TCA cycle during the light is due to the fact that the assimilatory power is adequate to ensure that traffic from phosphoglyceric acid is primarily in the direction of hexose synthesis.

There is also evidence that both elements of the "assimilatory power" generated in the light might leave the chloroplast and substitute for ATP and reduced nucleotides normally generated in respiratory reactions. Thus the effects of light in inducing glucose absorption in *Chlorella* (Kandler, 1954, 1955) and salt movements in leaves (Arisz, 1956; van Lookeren Campagne, 1957) may be attributed to the generation of ATP in the light. The alternative explanation, that mitochondrial oxidation of nucleotides reduced in the chloroplasts was providing the energy, was clearly ruled out in van Lookeren Campagne's and Kandler's experiments. Another important effect of light, that on nitrate reduction in green cells, was discovered by Warburg and Negelein (1920). Although nitrate may be reduced to ammonia at the expense of respiratory energy in nongreen parts of plants (Chapter 9), the striking effects of light on the process in leaves, and particularly on nitrite reduction, constitute the best evidence we have for a passage of reduced nucleotides from the chloroplast *in vivo* (Van Niel *et al.*, 1955; Kessler, 1957; Vanecko and Varner, 1955). As in all experiments of this kind, it is difficult to exclude the possibility that the light reaction has been consummated in glucose production and that this, rather than the assimilatory power, is the direct source of the energy for the reduction. However, in Kessler's experiments on nitrite reduction, this possibility was excluded since reduction was shown to occur anaerobically and in a CO_2-free atmosphere. A variety of reductive events in which reduced nucleotides generated in the light are the intermediate electron carriers has been accomplished *in vitro* with isolated chloroplasts and more or less purified dehydrogenases (see Vishniac *et al.*, 1957, for a review). It will be recalled that Evans and Nason (1953) were able to demonstrate nitrate reduction in a reconstructed system of chloroplasts and a nitrate reductase. Kessler's experiments indicate that, in the algae he examined, NO_3' reduction is less directly linked to the photochemical reactions than that of NO_2', since little reduction of NO_3' occurred in the light unless CO_2 was also present. In addition, there appears to be a requirement for ATP, as well as reduced nucleotide, in NO_2' reduction.

The demonstration that nitrite can function as an oxidant for photochemically produced reductants heightens the possibility that these reductants are also the substrates for "respiratory" electron transfer outside the chloroplasts and O_2 uptake in the light. Recent work has emphasized the complexity of electron-transfer sequences in the chloroplasts themselves and that some of the steps, including the final transfer to O_2, might be light-stimulated (e.g., Nieman and Vennesland, 1959). The effects of light on the rates of respiratory gas exchanges had been the subject of experiment and debate long before there was any means of direct measurement (see Rabinowitch, 1945, 1956). The two questions of interest here are (a) To what extent are the rates of respiratory gas exchange altered by the onset of photosynthesis? and (b) Are the reactions involving O_2 uptake and CO_2 in the light the same as those prevailing in the dark?

For those who had maintained that respiration continues

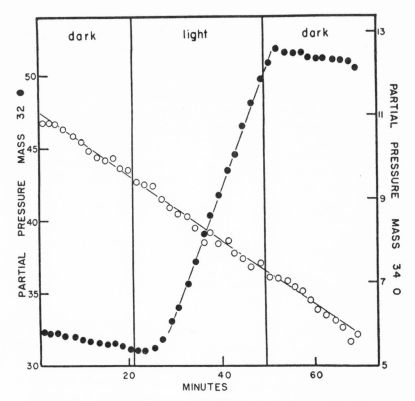

FIGURE 27.—Simultaneous determination of the photosynthetically produced oxygen (Mass 32) and respiratory uptake of oxygen (Mass 34) in barley leaf. Gas phase $N_2/CO_2/O_2$ 93:5:2. (Daly and Brown, 1954.) (Courtesy Archives Biochem. Biophys.)

unchanged on transferring green cells from dark to light, the results of Brown's group in Minnesota were most reassuring (Figure 27). By an elegant application of mass spectrometer technique, in which O_2 output from photosynthesis was distinguished from O_2 uptake in respiration, it was shown (Brown, 1953) that at moderate and low light intensities the O_2 uptake of *Chlorella pyrenoidosa* and of several higher plant tissues does, in fact, continue at an unchanged pace in the light. It should be remembered, however, that in the leaves, cells without chloroplasts might contribute in large measure to this O_2 uptake (see Chapter 6) and that in experiments with other algal types examples were found both of light-stimulated O_2 uptake and of light inhibition (Brown and Webster, 1953; Johnston and Brown, 1954).

It is recognized that photosynthetically produced O_2 might be preferentially utilized in respiration and that rapid fixation of respired CO_2 before it leaves the green cells would affect measurements of CO_2 output even when isotopic methods are used (see below). In some recent experiments Brown and Weiss (1959) have taken advantage of the properties of the alga *Ankistrodesmus braunii* and have further refined their calculations to arrive at rates of CO_2 production and consumption and of O_2 uptake and production at the absorptive sites. The conclusion was reached that, in this organism, CO_2 output was inhibited by light at all intensities but that O_2 uptake, while unaffected at low intensities, was stimulated in bright light. The results were discussed with reference to a model similar to that in Figure 26 and were shown to be in quantitative agreement with the mediation of a photochemically produced reductant in respiration.

Another way in which the influence of light on CO_2 output has been measured is by allowing respiratory substrates in the green cells to become labeled with C^{14} and then to compare $C^{14}O_2$ output in the light and dark. In elegant experiments with barley leaves, Weigl, Warrington, and Calvin (1951) showed that strong light did depress respiratory CO_2 production but suggested that refixation of this CO_2 in photosynthesis may have been large enough to account for the effect. Ryther (1955) placed a similar interpretation on his experiments with the alga *Dunaliella*. Steemann-Nielsen (1955) concluded from results with *Chlorella* that the light-suppression of CO_2 output cannot be entirely accounted for in this way and must be ascribed to an internal interaction of photosynthesis and respiration. In work with wheat, Krotkov, Runeckles, and Thimann (1958) concluded that light enhanced CO_2 production but that in *Kalanchoe* and pea it was usually reduced.

Clearly there are already a variety of responses to be accounted for, and only a very flexible system could accommodate them all. Perhaps the most that can be said at present is that very different effects on O_2 uptake and CO_2 output may result from illuminating green cells; the rate of O_2 uptake, at least at low light intensities, may be completely unaltered in higher plants, while CO_2 output is drastically lowered. Clearly there is not simply an effect of light on the over-all respiration rate. Photosynthetically produced reductants almost certainly replace respiratory ones to some extent, and, perhaps as a result of this, the principal decarboxylative events in the light may be different from those normally occurring in the dark (Stiller, 1958).

Recent observations of Zelitch (1958) on the effects of inhibitors of glycolic oxidase in the light have lent further emphasis to the idea that O_2 uptake in the light, though its rate might be identical to that in a preceding dark period, might be due to the substitution of light-generated reductants. He has shown that, in the presence of inhibitors of glycolic oxidase, glycolate accumulated in the light in the amounts expected if it were normally oxidized and accounted for O_2 uptake in the light. Experiments with the mass spectrometer in which the effects of the inhibitors on O_2 uptake could be measured directly are urgently needed for the further exploration of these interesting results.

REFERENCES

Arisz, W. H. Protoplasma 46, 5 (1956).
Arnon, D. I. Science 122, 9 (1955).
Bassham, J. A., Shibata, K., and Calvin, M. Biochim Biophys. Acta 17, 332 (1955).
Bassham, J. A., Shibata, K., Steenberg, K., Bourdon, J., and Calvin, M. Jour. Am. Chem. Soc. 78, 4120 (1956).
Bidwell, R. G. S., Krotkov, G., and Reed, G. B. Can. J. Botany 33, 189 (1955).
Brown, A. H. Am. Jour. Botany 40, 719 (1953).
Brown, A. H., and Webster, G. C. Am. Jour. Botany 40, 753 (1955).
Brown, A. H., and Weis, D. S. Plant Physiol. 34, 224 (1959).
Burma, D. P., and Mortimer, D. C. Can. J. Biochem. Physiol. 35, 835 (1957).

Burris, R. H. Ann. Rev. Plant Physiol. **4,** 91 (1953).
Calvin, M., and Massini, P. Experientia **8,** 445 (1952).
Daly, J. M., and Brown, A. H. Arch. Biochem. Biophys. **52,** 380 (1954).
Evans, H. A., and Nason, A. Plant Physiol. **28,** 233 (1953).
Franck, J. Arch. Biochem. Biophys. **45,** 190 (1953).
Gibbs, M. Arch. Biochem. Biophys. **45,** 156 (1953).
Johnston, J. A., and Brown, A. H. Plant Physiol. **29,** 117 (1955).
Kandler, O. Zeitschr. Naturforsch. **9(b),** 625 (1954).
Kandler, O. Zeitschr. Naturforsch. **10(b),** 38 (1955).
Kessler, E. Planta **49,** 505 (1957).
Krotkov, G., Runeckles, V. C., and Thimann, K. V. Plant Physiol. **33,** 289 (1958).
Milhaud, G., Benson, A. A., and Calvin, M. Jour. Biol. Chem. **218,** 599 (1956).
Naylor, A. W., and Tolbert, N. E. Physiol. Plant. **9,** 220 (1956).
Nieman, R. H., and Vennesland, B. Plant Physiol. **34,** 255 (1959).
Rabinowitch, E. *Photosynthesis and Related Processes,* Interscience, New York: Vol. I (1945), Vol. II (Parts 1 and 2) (1956).
Ryther, J. H. Deep Sea Res. **2,** 134 (1955).
Steemann-Nielsen, E. Physiol. Plant. **8,** 945 (1955).
Stiller, M. L. Ph.D. Thesis, Purdue University, Lafayette, Indiana (1958).
Vanecko, S., and Varner, J. E. Plant Physiol. **30,** 388 (1955).
van Lookeren Campagne, R. N. Acta botanica Neerland. **6,** 543 (1957).
Van Niel, C. B., Allen, M. B., and Wright, B. E. Biochim. Biophys. Acta **12,** 67 (1953).
Vishniac, W., Horecker, B. L., and Ochoa, S. Adv. in Enzymol. **19,** 1 (1957).
Warburg, O., and Negelein, E. Biochem. Zeitschr. **110,** 66 (1920).
Weigl, J. W., Warrington, P. M., and Calvin, M. Jour. Am. Chem. Soc. **73,** 5058 (1951).
Zelitch, I. Jour. Biol. Chem. **233,** 1299 (1958).

Chapter 12

Relationships

to Fat Metabolism

Fats and related triglycerides are important, though minor, constituents of all living cells. When these highly saturated compounds are being produced, there are presumably temporary repercussions on the respiratory process. These repercussions become of major importance when fats are being laid down as food reserves in maturing seeds. A large number of plant species have seeds in which fats or oils are the major food reserve (Hilditch, 1956), and in many others there is a notable fat component. Sucrose is apparently the mobile precursor for the synthesis, and the conversion into fat involves reactions which have profound effects on the respiration of those tissues in which the change takes place, namely, the endosperm or cotyledon tissues of the maturing seeds. However, the conversion of carbohydrate into fat is accomplished not so much by a process completely different from normal respiration as by one which makes certain extensions on sequences already discussed and uses intermediates in a different manner.

The converse aspect of fat metabolism is seen during germination (see Murlin, 1933). Here the utilization of the reserve fat is the dominating catabolic event in the seedling during the rapid growth of the embryo. The immediate fate of the bulk of the fat is not, however, conversion to CO_2 and H_2O; instead we find a very efficient conversion of fat into carbohydrate, which leaves the cotyledons or endosperms and supports a typical carbohydrate respiration in the embryo proper (see, e.g., Yamada, 1955). The reactions by which this reformation of carbohydrate is brought about, a process, we may note, which is without parallel in mammalian tissues, constitute in large measure the respiration of the nonembryonic parts of fatty seedlings.

The present (though incomplete) understanding of the process of fat synthesis and breakdown in plants, the associated gas exchanges, and the relationships to other respiratory patterns has become possible only through the elucidation of the central importance of the acetyl unit and its derivation from longer-chain fatty acids by the process of β-oxidation. Excellent accounts of this process whereby currency in the form of acetyl-CoA is produced from acids such as palmitic by enzymes from mammalian mitochondria are given by Green (1954) and Lynen (1955). An outline of the fatty acid spiral is given below. The major steps, each catalyzed by particular enzymes, are:

1. Activation of the substrate acid by coenzyme A, through an adenylate derivative:

$$R \cdot CH_2 \cdot CH_2 \cdot COOH + CoA + ATP \rightleftarrows$$
$$R \cdot CH_2 \cdot CH_2 CO\text{-}CoA + AMP + PP$$

2. Dehydrogenation of the acyl-CoA (acyl-CoA dehydrogenase):

$$R \cdot CH_2 \cdot CH_2 \cdot CO\text{-}CoA \rightleftarrows R \cdot CH{=}CH \cdot CO\text{-}CoA + 2H$$

3. Hydration of the unsaturated acyl-CoA (crotonase or acyl-CoA hydrase):

$$R \cdot CH{=}CH \cdot CO\text{-}CoA + H_2O \rightleftarrows R \cdot CHOH \cdot CH_2 \cdot CO\text{-}CoA$$

4. Dehydrogenation of the hydroxy acid–CoA derivative (hydroxy acyl-CoA dehydrogenase):

$$R \cdot CHOH \cdot CH_2 \cdot CO\text{-}CoA \rightleftarrows R \cdot CO \cdot CH_2 \cdot CO\text{-}CoA + 2H$$

5. Thiolysis of the β-keto acyl-CoA derivative (thiolase):

$$R \cdot CO \cdot CH_2 \cdot CO\text{-}CoA + CoA \rightleftarrows R \cdot CO\text{-}CoA + CH_3 \cdot CO\text{-}CoA$$

6. R.CO-CoA re-enters reactions 2–5, and successive units of acetyl-CoA are generated.

UTILIZATION OF FAT IN GERMINATING SEEDS

The first biochemical step in the utilization of fat is presumed to be hydrolysis. However, in tissues which have been carefully examined, e.g., *Citrullis vulgaris* (Crombie and Comber, 1956), in spite of the precipitous fall in the amount of fat during germination, its utilization may be completed without the appearance of noticeable amounts of free fatty acids or of shorter homologues which may have appeared to be likely intermediates in further breakdown (see also White, 1958, and Boatman and Crombie, 1958). Neither does glycerol, the other product of hydrolysis by lipase, accumulate to the extent anticipated if uncomplicated hydrolysis occurred. However, it has been positively identified by Desveaux and Kogane-Charles (1956) in castor-bean and flax seedlings and shown to rise strikingly during their germination.

The fate of the fatty acids will be discussed first. In addition to lipase (whose activity in plants has been recognized for many years), another well-known constituent of several fatty seeds is lipoxidase. The function of this enzyme, which accomplishes the peroxidation of unsaturated fatty acids with the uptake of O_2 (see Chapter 4) is at present obscure. It will be recalled that most natural fats contain mixtures of triglycerides; although in particular species one or another fatty acid usually predominates, the available evidence does not indicate that there is any orderly discrimination during utilization (Boatman and Crombie, 1958). The unsaturated acids present some unresolved problems. However, Simmons and Quackenbush (1954) showed that in maturing soy beans linoleic and linolenic acids might be derived from a less unsaturated precursor, oleic acid, and White's (1958) data indicate that linoleic may be converted into oleic acid during germination of cotton seed. The fatty acid dehydrogenases described by Franke and Frehse (1957) may be of importance here.

Stumpf and his colleagues have been particularly successful in isolating enzymes which induce the actual breakdown of the fatty acid chain and which must be considered as potentially active *in vivo*. It should be noted that in many of these experiments palmitate was used as substrate, and very small amounts, of the order of 0.1 micromole, were supplied. Therefore the oxidations which were induced were not large enough to permit manometric measurement; the reactions were followed instead by determining the fate of C^{14} incorporated at strategic places in the substrate molecule.

The first such enzyme was described by Humphreys *et al.* (1954). It was present in the microsomal fraction from germinating peanuts and produced $C^{14}O_2$ from COOH-labeled palmitate and also, to a smaller degree, from the internal carbon atoms in the chain. This enzyme was later made soluble by sodium choleate treatment (Humphreys and Stumpf, 1955). Although DPN was necessary for conversion of internal carbons to CO_2, CoA was not stimulatory, and the reactions of the TCA cycle apparently played no part in the oxidation. A second enzyme (Stumpf, 1956), "saturated fatty acid peroxidase," attacked acids such as myristic, palmitic, and stearic. In the presence of enzymatically generated H_2O_2 the carboxyl carbon was released as CO_2 and a long-chain fatty aldehyde resulted. Up to this time there had been no parallel, from *in vitro* experiments, for the β-oxidation sequence outlined above. However, it already appeared from work with intact tissues that the β-oxidation sequence must also be important in plant materials. The evidence came not only from experiments in which labeled acid substrates were used in synthesis and breakdown in fatty seedlings (Newcomb and Stumpf, 1953) but also from quite an unexpected quarter, that of investigations of the effectiveness of alkyl derivatives of growth-regulating compounds (Fawcett *et al.*, 1954; Wain and Wightman, 1954).

It came then as something of a vindication for comparative biochemistry when the β-oxidation of palmitate and butyrate was demonstrated in peanut mitochondria by Stumpf and Barber (1956). Mitochondria which previously had been shown to be incapable of oxidizing fatty acids were now found, in the presence of appropriate cofactors, including CoA and a TCA-cycle intermediate, to convert C^{14}-labeled palmitate to $C^{14}O_2$ in a manner consistent with β-oxidation. (We may note that the effectiveness of added CoA in the oxidations by plant mitochondria [see also Beevers and Walker, 1956] has no counterpart in the work with intact mammalian mitochondria.) Important facts which justify the conclusion that breakdown was by β-oxidation, followed by oxidation of the acetyl unit to CO_2 and H_2O in the TCA cycle, are as follows:

a. The essentiality for ATP and CoA, components of the activating system.
b. The essentiality for a TCA-cycle acid as sparker.
c. The inhibition of $C^{14}O_2$ release by malonate.
d. The incorporation of C^{14} from substrate fatty acid into TCA-cycle intermediates.
e. Acetate was itself oxidized with more rapid conversion of the carboxyl than the methyl carbon to CO_2, and carbons 2 and 3 of palmitate appeared at the predicted rates (Table XXXV).

Whatever the importance of the other sequences of fatty

TABLE XXXV

COMPARISON OF THE EFFECT OF ODD VS. EVEN CARBON-LABELING ON THE RATE OF APPEARANCE OF C^{14} IN RESPIRATORY CO_2 (STUMPF AND BARBER, 1956)

SUBSTRATE*	% OF TOTAL C^{14} IN $BaC^{14}O_3$		
	30 Min.	60 Min.	120 Min.
Acetate-1-C^{14}	4.4	12.0	36
Acetate-2-C^{14}	2.2	6.3	22
Ratio odd/even	(2.0)	(1.9)	(1.6)
Palmitate-3-C^{14}	18.0	36.0	53
Palmitate-2-C^{14}	1.1	4.2	15
Ratio odd/even	(16.5)	(8.6)	(3.5)

* The named substrate was added to peanut mitochondria with cofactors and α-ketoglutarate as cosubstrate.

acid breakdown, it now seems clear that β-oxidation can occur in plant mitochondria. The repercussions of an operating β-oxidation sequence on the gas exchanges of the cells should be recognized. For each molecule of C_{18} acid converted to acetyl-CoA, 16 pairs of electrons are transferred. The reoxidation of the electron acceptors in the mitochondria would result in the uptake of 4 molecules of O_2 and presumably the generation of ATP. No CO_2 is released in the process.

The fate of acetyl-CoA. Although one possible fate of acetyl-CoA from fatty acid breakdown, as indicated by the experiments of Stumpf and Barber, is complete oxidation to CO_2 and H_2O, it has recently become apparent that it may suffer a less untimely fate. It was already known that complete conversion to CO_2 is not the fate of fatty acids in germinating seeds. Instead there is a net production of sugars; in castor bean, for example, during germination a gram of sucrose accumulates in the endosperm for each gram of fat disappearing (Desveaux and Kogane-Charles, 1952), and this in spite of the fact that sugars are being used in the active metabolism of the embryo proper. Moreover it has been established (Beevers, 1957) that when acetate is provided to endosperm slices, at least 50% of its total carbon may be converted into sucrose. It should be clear that no *net* synthesis of a likely glucose precursor such as oxalacetate from acetate is possible through the agency of the TCA cycle, since, for each entering C_2 unit, 2 molecules of CO_2 are released. The glyoxylate cycle described by Kornberg and Krebs (1957), on the basis of information from microorganisms, provides a pathway by which such a net synthesis of dicarboxylic acid can be achieved (Figure 28). Kornberg and Beevers (1957) were able to show that the reactions of this cycle occur in castor-bean endosperm. The crucial enzymes are (a) isocitritase, which, by splitting isocitrate to succinate and glyoxylate, bypasses the α-ketoglutarate step and thus two oxidative decarboxylations:

$$\text{Isocitrate} \xrightarrow[\text{Isocitritase}]{} \text{Succinate} + \text{glyoxylate}$$

THE GLYOXYLATE CYCLE

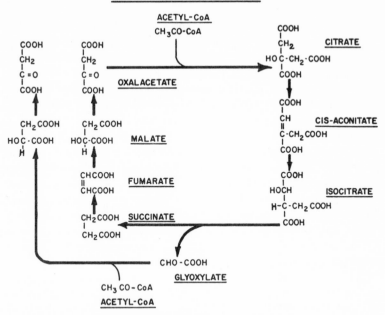

FIGURE 28.—Reactions of the glyoxylate cycle.

and (b) malate synthetase, by which malate is formed from glyoxylate and acetyl-CoA:

Glyoxylate + acetyl-CoA + H_2O → Malate + CoA

These enzymes have now been studied in some detail and shown to be widespread in germinating fatty seeds (Carpenter and Beevers, 1959); Yamamoto and Beevers, 1960; Bradbeer and Stumpf, 1959). Isocitritase, in particular, seems to be confined to tissues in which conversion of fat to carbohydrate is occurring; it appears strikingly during germination and is absent from the embryonic axis and maturing seeds on the parent plant. Malate synthetase is also particularly active in fatty seedlings, and it too increases sharply during germination and disappears later. The amounts of these enzymes which can be extracted are commensurate with their being part of the mechanism by which sugars are produced from fat.

Experiments with tissue slices have indicated clearly that such a sequence, in conjunction with a reversal of glycolysis (Benedict and Beevers, 1960), does indeed operate in the conversion of fats into carbohydrate (Figure 29). Thus, in the utilization of labeled acetate it has been found that organic acids, principally malate and citrate, are the earliest products and that the relative amount of C^{14} in the organic acid fraction decreases as that in sucrose increases (Canvin and Beevers, 1960). Furthermore, the distinctive labeling patterns in malate and glucose are those predicted from the operation of the glyoxylate cycle and reversed glycolysis (Bradbeer and Stumpf, 1959; Canvin and Beevers, 1960). The conversion of succinate and malate into sucrose has also been demonstrated (Canvin and Beevers, 1960), and the var-

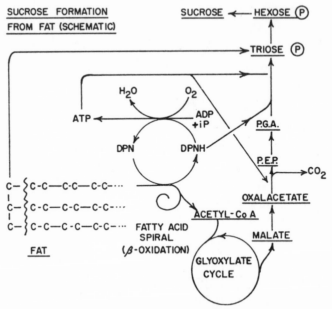

FIGURE 29.—Summary of reactions by which fat is probably converted to sugar.

ious features of the utilization of these compounds are in ac-
cordance with the above proposal. Experiments with labeled
pyruvates (Neal and Beevers, 1960) have shown that the entry
into the glycolytic sequence is at the level of phospho-enol
pyruvate, and the requisite enzymes for converting oxalacetate to sucrose by this sequence have been shown to be present (Benedict and Beevers, 1960). The driving force for the
reductive reaction at the triose phosphate stage arises no
doubt during the oxidation of the fatty acids to acetyl-CoA
(Figure 29).

The following reactions summarize the steps by which
sucrose appears to be formed from fatty acid:

$$C_{16}H_{32}O_2 \xrightarrow{\text{Fatty acid spiral}} 8\ CH_3\,CO\text{-}CoA + 28\ [H]$$

$$8\ CH_3\,CO\text{-}CoA \xrightarrow{\text{Glyoxylate cycle}} 4\ \text{Oxalacetate} + 24\ [H]$$

$$4\ \text{Oxalacetate} \rightarrow 4\ \text{Phospho-enol pyruvate} + 4\ CO_2$$

$$4\ \text{Phospho-enol pyruvate} + 8\ [H] \rightarrow \text{Sucrose}$$

Over all: $C_{16}H_{32}O_2 + 11\ O_2 \rightarrow C_{12}H_{22}O_{11} + 4\ CO_2 + 5\ H_2O$

$$R.Q. = 4/11 = 0.36$$

If this system were operating to the exclusion of other reactions, we would anticipate a maximum of 75% conversion
of acetate or fatty acid carbon into sucrose, which is in fact
closely approximated *in vivo*. It would be self-sufficient energetically and predict the observed patterns of utilization
of labeled substrates and would lead to an over-all R.Q. of
0.36, which is close to that observed in the endosperm itself
(Yamada, 1955).

Utilization of glycerol. The oxidation of glycerol has been
achieved in cell-free preparations from peanut by Stumpf
(1955). Two components were required: a soluble supernatant fraction which contained glycolytic enzymes, and a mitochondrial fraction. In addition to the enzymes of the TCA
cycle, the particles apparently contained a kinase for the
glycerol and a cytochrome-c-linked α-glycerol phosphate de-

hydrogenase. Evidence was presented for the occurrence of the following partial reactions:

Glycerol → Glycerol phosphate → Triose phosphate →

$$\text{Pyruvate} \rightarrow \text{TCA cycle} \rightarrow CO_2 + H_2O$$

For maximum rates of the over-all conversion of glycerol-1-C^{14} to $C^{14}O_2$ the following cofactors were required: ATP, TPP, DPN, and Mg^{++} as well as α-ketoglutarate as cosubstrate (Table XXXVI). It was found that fluoride, an inhibitor of enolase, depressed the conversion to CO_2 very strongly and that malonate was inhibitory. As further support for the suggestion that glycerol oxidation involved conversion, by way of glycolysis, to pyruvate and the TCA cycle, it was shown that during co-oxidation with α-ketoglutarate, acids of the TCA cycle became labeled with C^{14}.

The utilization of glycerol by tissue slices has been investigated by Beevers (1956). Tissues other than fatty seedlings can oxidize glycerol, but high rates of conversion are found, for example, in castor-bean cotyledons. As in Stumpf's cell-free system, fluoride inhibited the oxidation. Malonate slowed down oxidation and, at the same time, ethanol-2-C^{14}

TABLE XXXVI

OXIDATION OF GLYCEROL-1-C^{14} TO $C^{14}O_2$ BY EXTRACTS OF
PEANUT COTYLEDONS (STUMPF, 1955)

Components	Total CPM as $BaC^{14}O_3$
Complete*	12,500
Without mitochondria	0
Without soluble fraction	0
Without ATP	56
Without Mg^{++}	6,500
Without α-ketoglutarate	600
Without TPP	1,420
Without DPN	8,500
Complete + malonate (0.1 M)	1,250
Complete + fluoride (0.01 M)	60

* The complete mixture contained mitochondria, soluble protein fraction, the cofactors ATP, Mg^{++}, TPP, DPN, and α-ketoglutarate as cosubstrate, with 0.4 micromoles (10^5 c.p.m.) glycerol-1-C^{14}.

was produced; thus pyruvate was implicated as a normal intermediate in oxidation. Only about one quarter of the glycerol supplied to cotyledons was converted to CO_2; the bulk of the remainder was recovered from the tissue as sucrose. In endosperm slices the proportion which is oxidized is even less. It was shown that the hexose units in the sucrose had been formed by condensation of two intact 3-carbon units from glycerol. The evidence is therefore strong, from *in vivo* experiments also, that glycerol is converted into a glycolytic intermediate, triose phosphate, and that this may either be oxidized or, what is apparently more likely in tissues converting fat to carbohydrate, condensed by aldolase to yield hexose units.

We may note that, in comparison to the utilization of the rest of the fat molecule, conversion of glycerol to sugar will result in only minor contributions to the gas exchanges; the only oxidative step is that from glycerol phosphate to triose phosphate.

The production of fats. Here again we find that contributions from Stumpf's laboratory are pioneering ones. Experiments in which labeled acetate was supplied to peanut slices showed that it was incorporated into long-chain fatty acids (Newcomb and Stumpf, 1953). Later, Gibble and Kurtz (1956) isolated some of the long-chain fatty acids from flax seedlings which had been exposed to acetate-1-C^{14}. Measurements of the C^{14} content of a few of the terminal carbons removed in turn by Schmidt degradation showed that the odd-numbered ones were much more highly radioactive than the rest. Thus it was clear that the fatty acids in the fat had been produced by multiple condensation of acetate units in accord with a reversal of the fatty acid spiral. There are now numerous records of experiments in which, as a result of providing acetate to plant cells, C^{14}-labeled fats appear as one of the products (e.g., Coppens, 1956; Tokarskaya and Kuzin, 1956).

In 1957, Stumpf and Barber reported that enzymatic synthesis of fatty acids had been achieved with avocado particles. ATP, CoA, and Mn^{++} were essential components of the medium, both carbon atoms of radioactive acetate were utilized, and the fatty acids were recovered, initially, in an esterified form. We may note that Crombie's (1956) work on the maturing kernel of oil palm had indicated that free fatty acids do not necessarily accumulate in intact tissues during the deposition of fat; the indications are that esterification with glycerol keeps pace with acid formation. No information is available from plants about this important step; in some analogous systems the fatty acids are apparently transferred from their CoA derivatives directly to the alcohol part of the ester. However, since only acids of particular sizes are found in natural fats, some degree of specificity must be imputed to the esterification process.

In more recent work with enzymes from acetone powders of avocado particles, Squires et al. (1958) and Mudd and Stumpf (1960) have established further details about fatty acid synthesis. Particularly interesting are the requirement for TPN and also the stimulatory effect of bicarbonate. Recent work with mammalian enzymes had brought to light these requirements, which, in addition to the requirement for soluble enzymes, sustain the suggestion that the synthesis of fatty acids does not take place by a simple reversal of the β-oxidation sequence. The TPN requirement is interesting because enzymes of the β-oxidation sequence are DPN-specific. The bicarbonate is required in the carboxylation of acetyl-CoA to malonyl-CoA, which is an essential intermediate; the previously incorporated CO_2 is lost during the subsequent condensation reactions (Wakil, 1960). It should be noted also that Sissakian and his coworkers (1958), in emphasizing the diverse enzymatic abilities of isolated (but perhaps not pure) chloroplasts, have shown that acetate-C^{14} is incorporated into fatty acids in their preparations.

When fatty acids are being produced from sugars, acetyl-CoA presumably arises from pyruvate oxidation rather than from acetate activation, (Figure 24). Acetate-activating enzymes have of course been isolated from plants (Millerd and Bonner, 1954), but these are not essential for fatty acid synthesis from natural precursors. By whatever detailed mechanism the condensation of acetyl-CoA units is achieved, it is clear that, for each such unit incorporated, reducing power to the tune of 4 electrons will be required. The uptake of O_2 during fat formation will be lowered to the extent that these electrons are diverted from their normal pathways of transfer to O_2. In the simplest case we can picture these electrons, plus one molecule of CO_2, being generated during the production of an acetyl-CoA unit from triose phosphate.

On this view the generation of acetyl-CoA would provide the reducing power for its own incorporation into fatty acid, and the process could be regarded as a sort of fermentation, with R.Q. $= \infty$. When O_2 is present, oxidase systems would then compete with the fatty acid–producing enzymes for the reduced coenzymes, and O_2 uptake would result, though at a lower level than that of CO_2 output. The R.Q. would then be greater than unity, as is typically observed during the period of fat deposition in maturing seeds (Burr and Miller, 1938). A suggestive piece of evidence to support this view is found in the results of Barmenkov (1955), working with sunflower. He reported that the fat content increased at the expense of carbohydrate more rapidly under anaerobic conditions than in air.

These considerations have been concerned with the expectations in the seed itself and have emphasized that sufficient is now known about the biochemistry to allow a clearer understanding of the gas exchanges involved than that which can be derived from considering the formulae of the starting and end products of the carbohydrate to fat conversion. Certainly in the seed which is developing in an immediate environment of ovary tissue, which is not itself producing fat, the respiratory gas exchanges actually due to the fat formation in the seed will be severely masked, and other reactions, such as protein synthesis in the seed itself, will complicate the picture.

REFERENCES

BARMENKOV, Y. P. Trudy Chkalovsk. Sel'skovkhoz Inst. 7, 113 (1955).
BEEVERS, H. Plant Physiol. 31, 440 (1956).
BEEVERS, H. Biochem. Jour. 66, 23P (1957).

BEEVERS, H., and WALKER, D. A. Biochem. Jour. 12, 114 (1956).
BENEDICT, C. R., and BEEVERS, H. In preparation.
BOATMAN, S. G., and CROMBIE, W. M. L. Jour. Exp. Botany 9, 52 (1958).
BRADBEER, C., and STUMPF, P. K. Jour. Biol. Chem. 234, 498 (1959).
BURR, G. O., and MILLER, E. S. Bot. Gaz. 99, 773 (1938).
CANVIN, D. T., and BEEVERS, H. Plant Physiol. 35, xv (1960).
CARPENTER, W. D., and BEEVERS, H. Plant Physiol. 34, 403 (1959).
COPPENS, N. Nature 177, 279 (1956).
CROMBIE, W. M. L. Jour. Exp. Botany 7, 181 (1956).
CROMBIE, W. M. L., and COMBER, R. Jour. Exp. Botany 7, 166 (1956).
DESVEAUX, R., and KOGANE-CHARLES, M. Ann. Inst. Natl. Recherches Agron. 3, 385 (1952).
DESVEAUX, R., and KOGANE-CHARLES, M. Compt. rend. 243, 1929 (1956).
FAWCETT, C. H., INGRAM, J. M. A., and WAIN, R. L. Proc. Roy. Soc. B142, 60 (1954).
FRANKE, W., and FREHSE, H., in Encyclopedia of Plant Physiology (M. STEINER, ed.), Vol. VII, Springer-Verlag, Berlin (1957).
GIBBLE, W. P., and KURTZ, E. B. Arch. Biochem. Biophys. 64, 1 (1956).
GREEN, D. E. Biol. Reviews 29, 330 (1954).
HILDITCH, T. P. The Chemical Constitution of Natural Fats, Wiley, New York (1956).
HUMPHREYS, T. E., NEWCOMB, E. H., BOKMAN, A. H., and STUMPF, P. K. Jour. Biol. Chem. 210, 941 (1954).
HUMPHREYS, T. E., and STUMPF, P. K. Jour. Biol. Chem. 213, 941 (1955).
KORNBERG, H. L., and BEEVERS, H. Biochim. Biophys. Acta 26, 531 (1957).
KORNBERG, H. L., and KREBS, H. A. Nature 179, 988 (1957).
LYNEN, F. Ann. Rev. Biochem. 24, 653 (1955).
MILLERD, A., and BONNER, J. Arch. Biochem. Biophys. 49, 343 (1954).
MUDD, J. B., and STUMPF, P. K. Fed. Proc. 19, 226 (1960).
MURLIN, J. R. Jour. Gen. Physiol. 17, 283 (1933).
NEAL, G. E., and BEEVERS, H. Biochem. Jour. 74, 409 (1960).
NEWCOMB, E. H., and STUMPF, P. K. Jour. Biol. Chem. 200, 233 (1953).
SIMMONS, R. O., and QUACKENBUSH, F. W. Jour. Am. Oil Chem. Soc. 31, 441 (1954).
SISSAKIAN, N. M. Adv. in Enzymol. 20, 201 (1958).
SQUIRES, C. L., STUMPF, P. K., and SCHMID, C. Plant Physiol. 33, 365 (1958).
STUMPF, P. K. Plant Physiol. 30, 55 (1955).
STUMPF, P. K. Jour. Biol. Chem. 223, 643 (1956).
STUMPF, P. K., and BARBER, G. A. Plant Physiol. 31, 304 (1956).
STUMPF, P. K., and BARBER, G. A. Jour. Biol. Chem. 227, 407 (1957).
TOKARSKAYA, V. I., and KUZIN, A. M. Biokhimiya 21, 816 (1956).
WAIN, R. L., and WIGHTMAN, F. Proc. Roy. Soc. B142, 525 (1954).
WAKIL, S. J. Fed. Proc. 19, 227 (1960). ·
WHITE, H. B. Plant Physiol. 33, 218 (1958).
YAMADA, Y. Sci. Papers Coll. Gen. Educ., Univ. Tokyo 5, 149 (1955).
YAMAMOTO, Y., and BEEVERS, H. Plant Physiol. 35, 102 (1960).

Index